WORLD FACTS AND TRENDS

Also by John McHale:
The Future Of The Future
The Ecological Context

WORLD FACTS AND TRENDS

By John McHale

Second Edition

The Macmillan Company, New York, New York
Collier-Macmillan Limited, London

The Macmillan Company
866 Third Avenue, New York, N.Y. 10022
Collier-Macmillan Canada Ltd.,
Toronto, Ontario

Library of Congress Catalog Card
Number: 70-186436

First Printing

Printed in the United States of America

CONTENTS

PREFACE

The first version of *World Facts and Trends* was prepared as an internal working document, in consultation with the American Division of the World Academy of Art and Science, for use in two related conferences:

1. Nobel Symposium 14, Stockholm, Sweden, 1969: *The Place of Value in a World of Facts.*
2. International Joint Conference of the American Geographical Society and the World Academy of Art and Science, New York City, U.S.A., 1970: *Environment and Society in Transition: Scientific Developments, Social Consequences, Policy Implications.*

As the demand for this initial document has exceeded its original audience and purpose, this second edition has been revised and expanded for more general distribution. Noting that many requests had come from teachers and students, the material has been reorganized so that it may be used as an introductory text focusing on the interrelationships of key trends at the world level. In this regard, "the facts" themselves are not as important as their consideration within the overall global context. The present emphasis on physical trends (rather than social and cultural) will be adjusted in further editions.

It should be underlined that it is *not intended as an exhaustive compilation* of such factual and trend materials—but it endeavors to present in a compact and usable form a *basic* selection of those items which may be most relevant to the discussion of its major themes.

Acknowledgment should be given to those staff members and students at the Center for Integrative Studies who contributed in various ways to this work, i.e., the major critical support of my colleague, Magda Cordell; research supervision and graphics, Eric Bartelt; student research, Joseph Hryvniak and Richard Stevens; and secretarial supervision, Rosalind Forse.

I am also grateful for the valuable comments and suggestions given by various participants at the above conferences and other users of this book, and for the continued interest of Dr. Boris Pregel, President of the American Division of the World Academy of Art and Science, and Professor Harold Lasswell, Chairman of the World University Council (WAAS), who formed the original advisory committee.

THE CONTEXT OF CHANGE

The last third of the twentieth century has become increasingly characterized as the age of critical transition, revolution, and discontinuity. In this situation, two major aspects of change are now crucial. One is the explosive growth in man's actual and potential capacities to interfere on a large scale with the natural environmental processes. The other is the lag in conceptual orientation toward these capacities and in the cognitive understanding of the social processes through which we may manage change more effectively. In both cases, the conceptual grasp of the rate and magnitude of ongoing changes and their potential consequences is one of our survival imperatives.

Our present waves of change differ from those of the recent past, not only in their quantitative aspects, but also in the quality and degree of their interrelationships. Where previously we might have dealt with relatively separate change factors within local and limited contexts, our present changes are now global in their spatial and quantitative dimensions. They are no longer isolable sequences of events separated in time, in numbers of people affected, and in the social and physical processes which are perturbed.

Global in scale, potentially affecting the physical balance of all life on the planet itself, and reaching into every aspect of individual human life and society, our ongoing change patterns now constitute a socioecological transition of evolutionary magnitude.

This ongoing series of "evolutionary" changes is, therefore, more specifically characterized by the simultaneity of changes occurring—by their swift interpenetration, increased feedback, and interdependence of one group of changes upon another.

INCREASED FREQUENCY. The new relationships and narrowing intervals between scientific discovery, technological development, and large-scale usage have become dramatically visible only in the past few decades.

RANGE AND SCALE. In addition to this reverberative increase in the frequency of change factors, many of the long-range and large-scale effects of various types of change on the environment, on social relations, on health, etc., have only become measurably apparent in the same period.

SIZE AND COMPLEXITY. The size, distribution, and complexity of many of our technological systems components is an important question here.

With increased size comes vastly increased dangers of hazard to larger numbers of people and larger areas of the environ. We have viewed recently an increasing number of near catastrophes in terms of oil spills, radiation leakages, large aircraft crashes, thalidomide-type chemical poisoning, large-scale power failures, etc.

EXPANDED IMPACT AND AWARENESS. Through increases in the speed of transportation and communication, the agencies of change (ideas, artifacts, techniques, images, and attitudes) are now diffused more rapidly and penetrate more swiftly into more aspects of human life.

DIFFERENTIAL RATES. Changes in technologies and ideas, as well as institutional and social changes, occur at varying rates and have different time spans of integration and acceptance, causing dissonance and discontinuity in and between various sectors of society.

The combination of the above factors gives less and less time for critical assessment of specific changes in themselves, and for individual and social adaptation. At one extreme, change becomes the

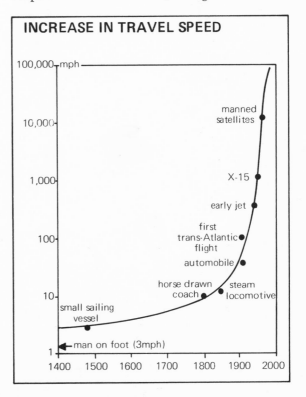

INCREASE IN TRAVEL SPEED

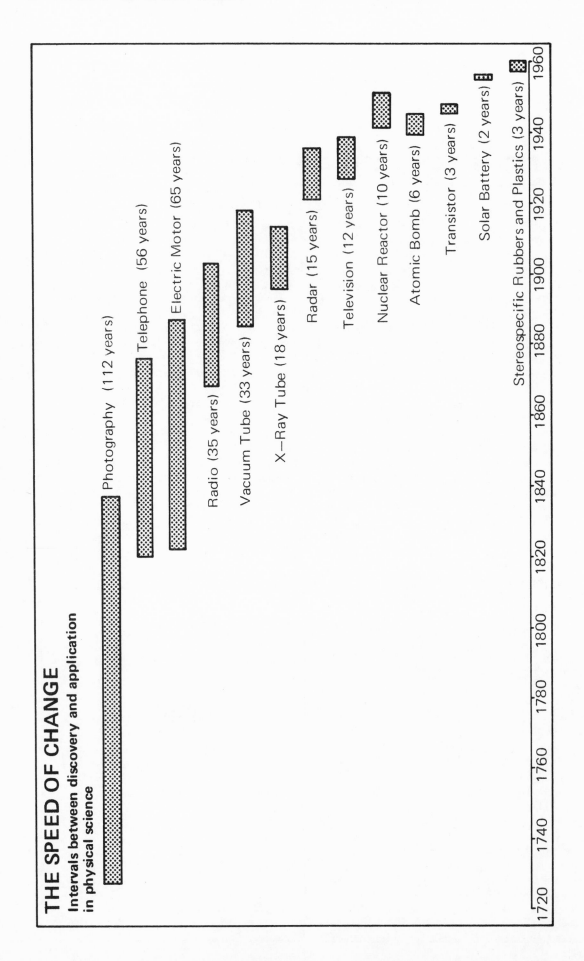

THE SPEED OF CHANGE

Intervals between discovery and application in physical science

Photography (112 years)

Telephone (56 years)

Electric Motor (65 years)

Radio (35 years)

Vacuum Tube (33 years)

X–Ray Tube (18 years)

Radar (15 years)

Television (12 years)

Nuclear Reactor (10 years)

Atomic Bomb (6 years)

Transistor (3 years)

Solar Battery (2 years)

Stereospecific Rubbers and Plastics (3 years)

1720 1740 1760 1780 1800 1820 1840 1860 1880 1900 1920 1940 1960

SHRINKING OF OUR PLANET BY MAN'S INCREASED TRAVEL AND COMMUNICATION SPEEDS AROUND THE GLOBE

YEAR	500,000 BC	20,000 BC	500 BC	300 BC	1,500 AD	1900 AD	1925	1950	1965
Required time to travel around the globe	A few hundred thousand years	A few thousand years	A few hundred years	A few tens of years	A few years	A few months	A few weeks	A few days	A few hours
Means of transportation	Human on foot (over, ice bridges)	On foot and by canoe	Canoe with small sail or paddles or relays of runners	Large sail boats with oars, pack animals, and horse chariots	Big sailing ships (with compass), horse teams, and coaches	Steam boats and railroads (Suez and Panama Canals)	Steamships, transcontinental railways, autos, and airplanes	Steamships, railways, auto jet and rocket aircraft	Atomic steamship, high speed railway, auto, and rocket-jet aircraft
Distance per day (land)	15 miles	15-20 miles	20 miles	15-25 miles	20-25 miles	Rail 300-900 miles	400-900 miles	Rail 500-1,500	Rail 1000-2000
Distance per day (sea or air)	None	20 by sea	40 miles by sea	135 miles by sea	175 miles by sea	250 miles by sea	3,000-6000 air	6000-9500 air	408,000 air
Potential state size	A small valley in the vicinity of a small lake	A small part of a continent	Small part of a continent	Large area of a continent with coastal colonies	Great parts of a continent with transoceanic colonies	Large parts of a continent with transoceanic colonies	Full continents & Transocean Commonwealths	The Globe	The globe and more

Communications	Word of mouth, drums, smoke, relay runners, and hand printed manuscripts prior to 1441 A.D.	① The Gutenberg 1441 printing press	② The rapid print Web 1863 newspaper press	③ The Bell 1876 telephone	④ The Marconi 1895 telegraph	⑤ First commercial 1920 radio broadcast	⑥ National 1950 Television	⑦ Transcontinental T.V. with the introduction 1965 of Early Bird satellite

THE RELATIVE SIZE OF THE WORLD AS TRAVEL TIME DECREASES

15,00 AD -1840 AD

1850-1930

Steam locomotives averaged 65 m.p.h. while steamships averaged 36 m.p.h.

1950's Propeller aircraft averaged 300-400 m.p.h.

1960's Jet passenger aircraft averaged 500-700 m.p.h.

The best average speed of horse drawn coaches on land and sailing ships at sea was approximately 10 m.p.h.

Rome was the only metropolis of over 1,000,000 people from this date forward until 1800 AD.

Rome's population declined by 30,000

5,000 years (300BC-1800AD) in which towns slowly evolved into cities, and then into metropolises.

Bubonic plague wiped out 1/4 of Europe's population

This toned area represents population growth

For the first time in history it began to be safe for men to live in large cities because of advances in medicine and sanitation. Life was made more secure and comfortable by the Industrial Revolution & mechanized farming

Man on foot = ⅓ mph.

Man on foot ⅓ mph.

5,000 years of villages & towns

and then

7,000 6,000 5,000 4,000 3,000 2,000 1,000 ◀BC AD▶ 100 200 300 400 500 600 700 800 900 1,000 1100 1200 1300 1400 1500 1600 1700 1800 1900 1965

manned Spacecraft

XB-70

Jet super sonic

Jet

First flight across the Atlantic

Automobile

Steam locomotive

Horse

Coach

Caravel=5 mph.

17,000 2,000 1,500 1,000 500 100 50 25 5 0

preferred norm; at the other, as associated with disruption and uncertainty, resistance to change becomes the mode.

Historically accustomed to slow and sporadic changes and the visible linearity of linked cause and effect, our latent assumption is that change is abnormal—that stability is the obverse of change, and that control lies with the alternation of these two states. Central, therefore, to our more effective understanding and management of the change process is the recognition that change and motion are constants—and that we may have stability within change.

There are three great evolutionary transitions in the human occupancy of the earth which are critical to our understanding of change:

1. THE AGRICULTURAL REVOLUTION. Man achieved a greater degree of long-range predictive control over his food supply through entering into a more directly symbiotic relation to intensive local land use. This gave rise to the early city civilizations, and so forth.
2. THE INDUSTRIAL REVOLUTION. This freed man from direct dependence on his own and animal muscle energies and, to a degree, freed him from local dependence on the land itself.
3. THE ECOLOGICAL REVOLUTION. In the past hundred years various successive and over-lapping strands of the industrial-social-electro-chemical and electronic revolutions have been developed, placing man and his systems at magni-tudes capable of large-scale interference with the overall ecological balance of the earth.

Many of our current dilemmas and change "syn-dromes" result from the fact that we have had more radical transformations of the human condition in the past one hundred years than may have occurred in all recorded history. Within three generations, massive series of scientific, technological, social, and economic changes have impacted one upon the other. Humanity has been thrust into a new world. Those ranges of scale, magnitude, and frequency of change have no reliable historical precedents or guidelines for their assessment and control.

As industrial civilization has expanded in this rela-tively brief period to encompass the entire planet, so have the problems that threaten human existence. Many of the problems themselves are not new nor are they intrinsically linked to the change processes which have occurred. What is new, and increasingly urgent, is their expanded dimensions. Their sheer size and complexity have, in many cases, been para-doxically compounded by the very measures which man has developed to combat them. By making humanity more secure against hunger and disease, we have added astronomically to our numbers; by shrinking the physical distance between peoples, we have increased the critical and complex interde-

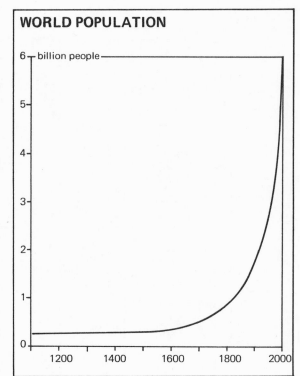

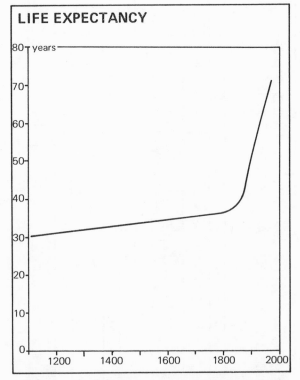

pendence of all human society; by communicating the material possibilities of a better life, we have enormously increased the expectations and demands by all people for access to these possibilities; and by the prodigal exploitation of our physical environs, we have now produced many grave imbalances in our life sustaining natural invironment.

More people now require more not only in quantity, but in far greater diversity and material quality than was ever dreamed of in any previous period. To keep pace with growing requirements, man has measurably extracted more materials, metals, minerals, and fuels from the earth and atmosphere in the past century than in all previous history.

This increase in human numbers and in the concomitant extraction and use of the huge amounts of materials and energy has also been accompanied by the massively accumulating by-products of these processes—the effluents and wastes which poison the air, overburden the lakes and rivers, and pollute the oceans and shores. Where more power also means more destructive power, we have the added menace of radioactive and other fallout from testing the "overkill" weapons which are now sufficient in quantity to destroy each living being many times over.

One of the key crisis points in our present transition in human development is where it begins to affect the balance of the planetary ecology. The question is now being asked: at which point could the explosive growth of the human species and its increased scale of "intrusions" into the biosphere, overwhelm the natural checks and balances? How long can the earth sustain such growth, absorb its by-products and ecological changes, and still remain a viable habitat for human life?

There are, obviously, no simple answers. In terms of the magnitudes of the change processes in themselves, we may even qualify both the curves and the rhetoric. Exponentials do not grow in isolation, as we often depict on graphs. Growth, size, and the frequency of change in itself are all relative measures. What may look like separate increases in one narrow frame of reference, such as our current span of time, may be a slowly changing distribution relative to a larger context or longer time span.

Our minimal assertion suggests that we accept

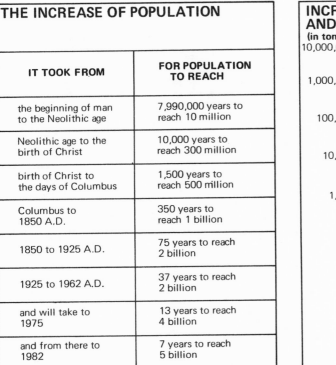

THE INCREASE OF POPULATION

IT TOOK FROM	FOR POPULATION TO REACH
the beginning of man to the Neolithic age	7,990,000 years to reach 10 million
Neolithic age to the birth of Christ	10,000 years to reach 300 million
birth of Christ to the days of Columbus	1,500 years to reach 500 million
Columbus to 1850 A.D.	350 years to reach 1 billion
1850 to 1925 A.D.	75 years to reach 2 billion
1925 to 1962 A.D.	37 years to reach 2 billion
and will take to 1975	13 years to reach 4 billion
and from there to 1982	7 years to reach 5 billion

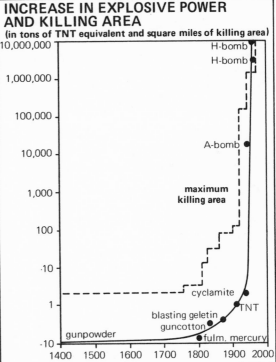

INCREASE IN EXPLOSIVE POWER AND KILLING AREA
(in tons of TNT equivalent and square miles of killing area)

some of the evidence as strongly indicative that we are indeed approaching the most critical juncture in human affairs in all history.

> In 1904 one man could stand before an audience of 5,000 and hope to be heard. Now it seems a trivial thing that one man can reach 50 million people in an evening—a multiplication of 10,0000. . . . Another increase of 10,000 to 100,000 has been achieved in the speed of mathematical computation. An electronic computer can do in minutes what would take a lifetime of hard calculation.
>
> The greatest multiplication, of course, has taken place in the energy at man's disposal. One thermonuclear warhead can release more energy than all the gunpowder and TNT exploded in all the wars of history. The multiplication factor, per pound, of material is about 50 million.[1]

It may also be underlined that the negatives inherent in the range and complexity of the prob-capabilities for human action which have been concomitantly developed. We have a greater variety of choices and options available to us, and greatly enlarged capacities to act decisively in many areas which have hitherto been beyond our control. Where the large-scale development of scientific and technological means has created a new kind of global reality, such means also permit the coexistence and choice of many different "realities" previously beyond our reach. Many of our individual and collective decisions need no longer be framed in terms of what we can do within traditional constraints, but in terms of what we choose to do within the range of our new possibilities and potentials. Our major questions regarding change, therefore, revolve around those changes in our institutions and societal procedures which will enable us to take advantage of our potentials.

MAN AND THE BIOSPHERE

Though we refer to the whole planet as our habitat, life on earth is restricted within a tenuous envelope of air, water, and soil which forms a thin film adhering closely to the planetary surface.

This fragile, enclosing shell of the forces which sustain life has been termed, variously, the biofilm, the ecosphere, and the biosphere. Its bounds are set vertically in the atmosphere at about 6¼ miles, downwardly to the known depths of the oceans around 36,000 feet, and into the first few thousand feet of the soil's surface itself where living organisms have been found. Its most densely populated region is just above and below sea level.

This relatively slight volume of air, water, and soil contains all living organisms which exist in the various systems of delicately balanced symbiotic relations. The fragility and close tolerances of many of these balances have become known to us, generally through their disruption, in recent times.

The "life space" of the biosphere is a unitary complex of organic relationships within the three layered system of the atmosphere, the hydrosphere, and the lithosphere. Within this system the "balance of life" conditions for the various forms of life are characterized by their highly specific "ecological niche" conditions. These conditions are comprised of the variable interactions of temperature, pressure, humidity, and electrical potential, and of the specific interface exchanges of liquid-solid, solid-gas, gas-liquid, etc., particular to each organism.

All life exchanges and interactions are further conditioned by energy radiation from various sources. The prime "motive power" for the overall system is from solar radiation received by the earth. To this major source of life sustaining radiation may be added the geothermal energies radiating outwardly to the surface from the earth's core, and the kinetic and potential energy of the planetary mass itself. The extent to which living organisms are also viably affected by other electromagnetic systems surrounding, and external to, the planet itself is little known at present.

Other constraints upon life forms (governing their optimal size, psychophysical configuration, life cycle, and metabolic rate) are gravity and temperature;

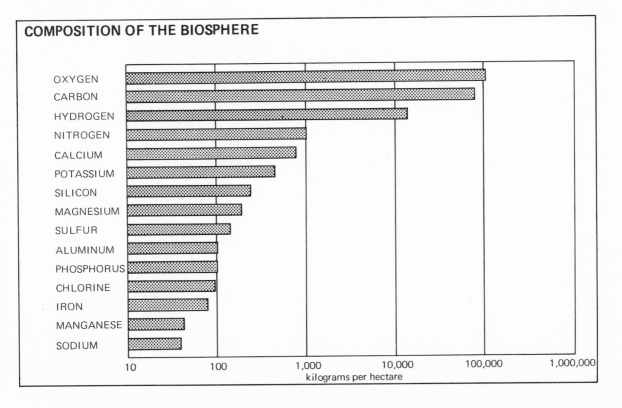

COMPOSITION OF THE BIOSPHERE

kilograms per hectare

e.g., the ways in which physical and structural effects and interchange pressures are affected by gravitational forces: the median temperature fluctuations of heat and radiation excitation on the earth's surface allow low temperature energy and materials exchange. These, in turn, relate to the frequency of exposure to solar radiation governed by the rotation of the earth, giving climatic variation, and to the distribution of other energy and material resources and cycles in the various sectors of the biosphere.

To these variables may be added other geographic features of altitude, continental mass relations, soil, vegetation distribution, marine environ conditions, etc.

This range of environmental conditions governing life has, so far, been in a sufficiently steady state to allow for long-term evolutionary changes to take place in various species, and yet it has provided a sufficient range and diversity of ecological niches to allow for a great variety of species. If we were to refer to an optimal ecological context, it would be defined within these terms of the preservation of a diversity of life milieu and a requisite variety of the species, types, and possible developmental ranges of life forms. These twin criteria of diversity and variety are, in this way, inseparable in terms of the evolving life balance in the biosphere.

In human terms, the planetary surface is relatively meager—approximately 197 million square miles, of which 57 million square miles is land and 140 million square miles is water. We live on a small island at the bottom of an ocean of air,

ATMOSPHERE

The composition of the atmosphere close to the earth's surface is mainly nitrogen, oxygen and argon in approximately 75, 23, and 1 per cent by volume. Other constituents, of less than 1 per cent are hydrogen, neon, krypton, xenon, radon, tritium, etc.

THE EARTH'S BIOSPHERE

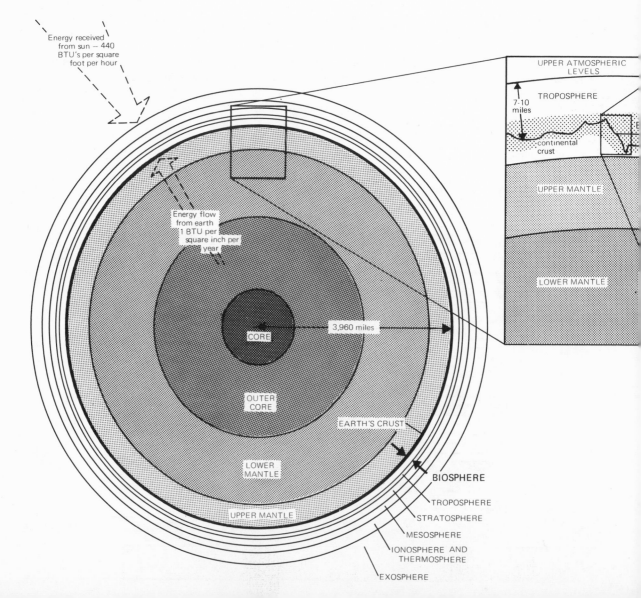

LITHOSPHERE

Elements which make up 98.58% of the earth's crust:

Oxygen	46.71%
Silicon	27.69%
Aluminum	8.07%
Iron	5.05%
Calcium	3.65%
Sodium	2.75%
Potassium	2.58%
Magnesium	2.08%

Other elements of present importance which occur in lesser percentages:

Nickel	0.02%
Tungsten	0.005%
Tin	0.0004%
Copper	0.010%

HYDROSPHERE

All available waters in the biosphere come from condensation of water vapor circulated in the atmospheric system -- as rain, snow, hail, dew, etc. The distribution of this evaporation/ precipitation/exchange cycle is global and links the terrestrial, atmospheric and marine environs in a massive interchange, not only of water, but of various other material elements injected into the different sectors of the cycle.

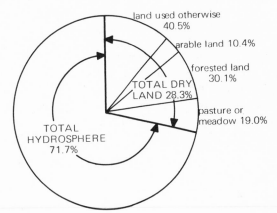

land used otherwise 40.5%

arable land 10.4%

forested land 30.1%

TOTAL DRY LAND 28.3%

pasture or meadow 19.0%

TOTAL HYDROSPHERE 71.7%

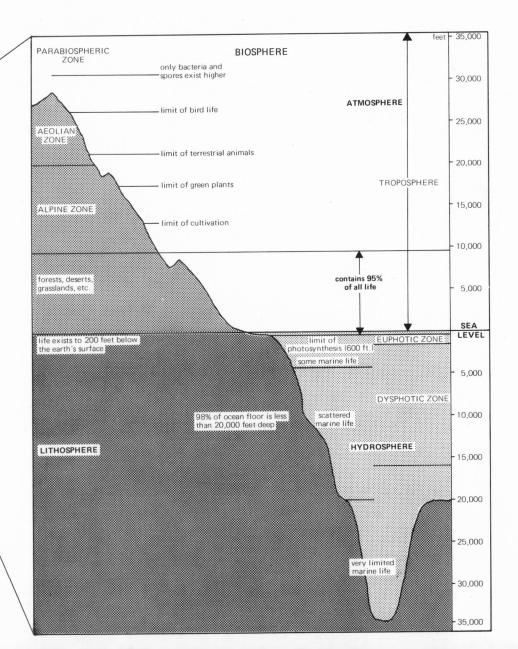

PARABIOSPHERIC ZONE

BIOSPHERE

only bacteria and spores exist higher

feet — 35,000

30,000

ATMOSPHERE

limit of bird life

25,000

AEOLIAN ZONE

limit of terrestrial animals

20,000

limit of green plants

TROPOSPHERE

15,000

ALPINE ZONE

limit of cultivation

10,000

contains 95% of all life

forests, deserts, grasslands, etc.

5,000

SEA LEVEL

life exists to 200 feet below the earth's surface

limit of photosynthesis (600 ft)

EUPHOTIC ZONE

some marine life

5,000

DYSPHOTIC ZONE

98% of ocean floor is less than 20,000 feet deep

scattered marine life

10,000

LITHOSPHERE

HYDROSPHERE

15,000

20,000

25,000

very limited marine life

30,000

35,000

surrounded by an ocean of water. Though most living forms are held close to the surface of the earth, the organic evolutionary process has been specifically characterized by the expansion of the "life zone" into the vertical and horizontal ranges of the biosphere.

One example of the enlargement of the human ecological niche through psychosocial extension has been characterized by Teilhard de Chardin as the addition of a "noosphere" layer. This concept of organized human thought now covering the globe as an organic process in the overall ecological system is physically demonstrable by our present world communications networks, by the enormously accelerated growth of human knowledge, and by parallel increases in the number of messages, meetings, journals, and so forth, ceaselessly circulating around the earth.

> The human goal that is implied in the concept of rational use of the biosphere is one that would seek a combination of a high material standard of living with a retention of a maximum variety of natural and man-made environments, including protection of non-human species and the values of wild nature. . . . Attainment of this goal would be possible only for a human population held at a compatible level, perhaps a level that could be described as an optimum abundance of people. The actual numbers involved in such an optimum population cannot be described in general terms, since they will vary with nations, cultures, and levels of technology. . . . From an ecological viewpoint also, this appears to be the only realistic goal for humanity, one in which the survival of free psychologically whole individuals remains possible . . . this orientation toward quality of life in place of quantity of people and of economic production is the only chance for retaining permanency of human civilization with full opportunities for individuals to develop their human potentials.[2]

THE BIOMASS

A series of preliminary assessments of the overall inputs and outputs of the planetary life mass has been initiated in recent years by various workers. Georg Borgstrom,[3] particularly, has explored the conceptual and substantive basis for computing "the global biomass" (human, animal, and plant) and his work gives certain unique insights into the magnitudes of interaction and interdependence of the various life forms.

Using what he terms population equivalents (P.E. units)—"based on a standard man weight of 70 kilograms as a unit and assuming a disposal of 70 grams of protein per day as a standard figure"—he underlines that though we center our discussion of food supply, e.g., around the feeding burden of the human population, we tend to forget that livestock, as consumers, take up a considerably larger proportion of food supply within the overall system.

The globe is not merely inhabited by 3 billion humans but, in order to maintain his present nutritional standard and to retain the type of agriculture now prevailing on earth, green plants must carry a feeding burden which is far in excess of the 3 billion humans, or what amounts to approximately 17.5 billion consumers—the livestock then accounting for 14.5 billion men. In spite of all mechanization used in some parts of the world, horses still account for a protein intake that corresponds to that of 653 million people: in other words, in consumptive force equal to that of the largest country of the world, namely, China. The Americas, with their 400 million people, as consumers represent only one-fourth of the intake of the pigs, as measured on a global scale. Cattle represent an intake of primary protein which is 2.5 times that of the population-rich Asian continent.[4]

In terms of the relative allocation of the biospheric resources, we may note that, in aggregate, the highly developed nations draw disproportionately upon these resources in comparison with the much larger numbers of people in the lesser developed countries. The industrialized nations consume approximately 80 percent of the world's income for only 20 percent of the world's people. For example, it has been estimated that the average relatively affluent American consumes from 30 to 200 times the total biospheric resources of one person in India. These comparisons are often drawn for food, material resources, etc., but ecologist LaMont Cole has given an interesting example in terms of an even more "basic" biospheric resource—oxygen:

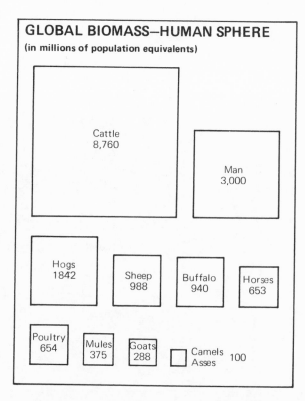

GLOBAL BIOMASS—HUMAN SPHERE
(in millions of population equivalents)

Cattle 8,760

Man 3,000

Hogs 1842

Sheep 988

Buffalo 940

Horses 653

Poultry 654

Mules 375

Goats 288

Camels Asses 100

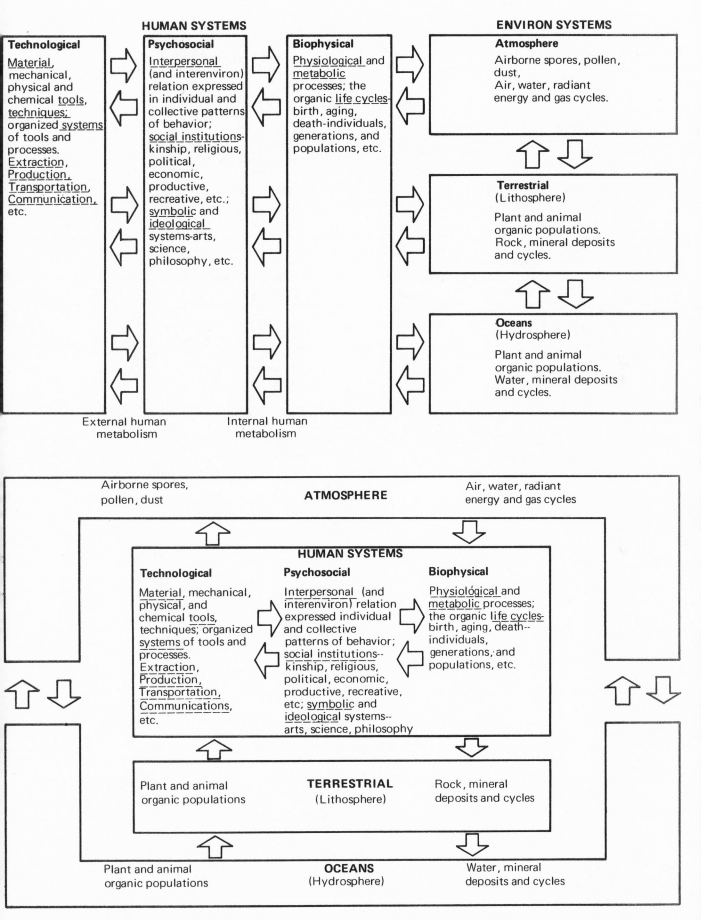

For the 48 coterminous United States I have attempted some calculations of the oxygen balance. I took the figures for production and imports of fossil fuels for the year 1966, corrected these for exports and non-combustible residues and calculated the amount of oxygen that would be required for their consumption. Then I made what I believe to be a good estimate of the amount of oxygen produced by photosynthesis within our borders that year. The amount of oxygen produced turned out to be not quite 60 percent of the amount consumed.[5]

Our scale of "intrusions" into the biosphere and our lack of specific knowledge regarding many of its crucial processes suggest that we will have to mount many such large-scale assessments and depth investigations. Much as we now talk about the need for "early warning systems" for the consequences of our technological developments, so we urgently need similar monitoring systems, particularly at the world scale, for the rational assessment and conservation of the resources of the biosphere.

THE GLOBAL ECOSYSTEM

In order to aid the conceptualization of this massive and complex system, we may employ such static diagrams as are presented here. It should be emphasized, however, that they are a schematic labeling device only and in no way reflect the relative scales and magnitudes or the dynamic nature of the whole system.

For convenience, the human systems and the physical environ systems have been separated out, and attention has been drawn to the ways in which the interactions of the technological and psychosocial sectors may be categorized as constituting the "external human metabolism"—comprising all the extractive, productive, distributive, and communicative processes sustaining human society. In the same mode the internal human metabolism results from both the psychosocial and biophysical processes of the individual organism(s).

It is recognized also that we need to extend the physical and biological concepts of ecology to include the social behaviors of man as critical factors in the maintenance of his dynamic ecological balance.

Nature is not only modified by human action as manifested in science and technology—through physical transformations of the earth to economic purpose—but also by those factors, less amenable to direct perception and measure, such as political-ethical systems, education, needs for social contiguity and communication, art, religion, etc. Such socio-cultural factors have played and will continue increasingly to play a considerable role in man's forward evolutionary trending and its effects on the overall ecology of the earth.

To emphasize this growing role of the man-made, and man-oriented, component systems, one of the diagrams of the global ecosystem has also been reoriented to place the human systems centrally within the overall process.

ENVIRON SYSTEM (S)

ATMOSPHERE

Of the earth's atmospheric shields, that most directly concerned with the biosphere is the tropospheric layer. This layer comprises about 70 percent of the air mass around the planet and is confined in a narrow band about six miles in width.

It functions as a great "cycling" reservoir that transforms and redistributes the various energies and materials that are swept up in its systemic flows. Within it move all the great wind systems that sweep around and ventilate the terrestrial biosphere, carrying all the water, gas, and material interchanges around the surface of the earth and playing a major role in the climatic cycle system. It has been calculated that a complete interchange of all the circulating air masses around the earth in the tropospheric layer takes about two years and that the passage of an "air parcel," or local air gaseous system, in the middle latitudes takes about one month.

Within this layer the condensation of water vapor also takes place, including within its interchange cycles all the available waters in the biosphere. The inward distributive pattern of this interchange is in the form of rain, snow, hail, dew, etc. The overall precipitation-evaporation-exchange cycle links the atmospheric, marine, and terrestrial areas of the biosphere through the exchange and redistribution not only of water and gases, but of a vast range of material particles swept up in different parts of the major environmental cycles. The latter process includes quantities of bacterial spores, seeds, and soil materials from wind erosion, dust of all kinds, and all the other materials which the natural and man-made earth processes pour into the air.

> . . . we have between five and six quadrillion tons of air. About half of it is concentrated in the lowest 18,000 feet, the part we use and reuse is restricted to the first few thousand feet, and we draw most heavily to sustain life on the air in the lowest ten feet.[6]

Where we may refer to the pollution of the atmosphere as a global, not local, problem, we may note that the dust particle masses and other materials noted above may be carried almost 3,000 miles by winds of only ten miles per hour before they are redeposited on the earth's surface. Natural dust and sandstorms are a common enough phenomenon: during the dust bowl storms of 1934, it was calculated that about 700 million tons of topsoil materials were eventually blown out to sea. In addition to such "natural" redistributions we now have the vast amounts of industrial and other by-product materials which are taken up in the same way and transported by the moving air masses to areas at some distance from their origins. This has already led to considerable difficulties in the control of atmospheric pollution, for example, in Europe where one nations's atmospheric pollutants originate in another national territory and are thereby removed from local national amelioration. There are now many cases of aerial, marine, and other environmental hazards, which will have to be dealt with by international controls and regulatory standards.

Close to the earth's surface, the composition of the atmosphere is nitrogen, oxygen, and argon in approximately 75, 23, and 1 percent by volume. Other constituents, amounting to less than a tenth of one percent, are hydrogen, neon, helium, krypton, xenon, radon, tritium, etc. We are generally not aware of the extent to which the atmosphere is freely "mined" of its elements in our various industrial and agri-industrial activities. These extractive uses are, of course, replaced by other parts of the natural cycles. But we have, as yet, no accurate and ongoing monitoring of the vastly enlarged scale at which this or that constituent may be in the process of extraction in excess of renewal by the ecosystem. Again, as the "local" atmosphere cannot in any defensible way belong exclusively within any national sovereignty in terms of unilateral regulation of its exploitation and pollution, we are now moving toward the urgent need for transnational regulatory agencies.

In addition to the circulatory and ventilating processes of the troposphere layer, there is its function, combined with the other layers of the atmosphere, in filtering the incoming solar and other radiations which bombard the earth. In broad terms, these layered shields admit the major parts of short-wave radiation to the earth but trap the outgoing long-wave radiation upward from the surface. This process works like a greenhouse screen, slowing up the dissipation of energies from the

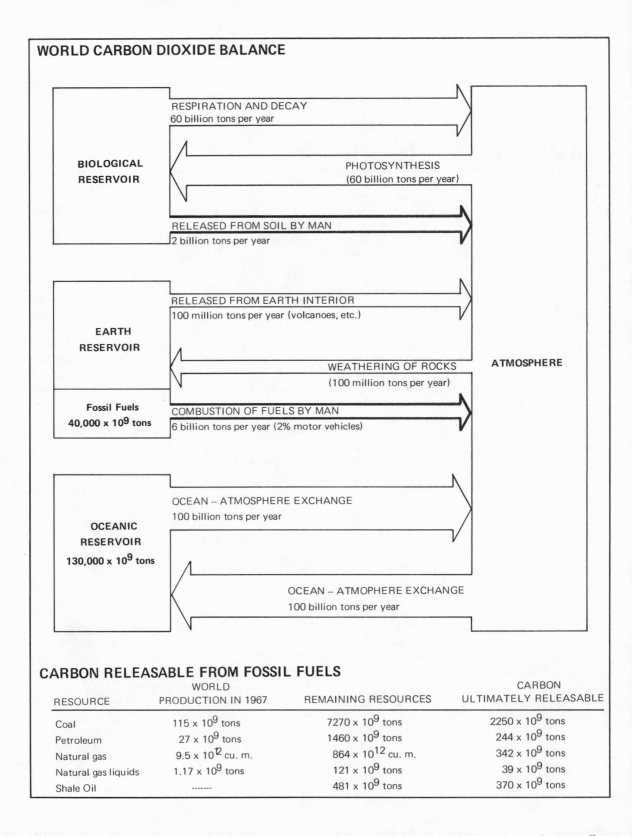

WORLD CARBON DIOXIDE BALANCE

BIOLOGICAL RESERVOIR

RESPIRATION AND DECAY
60 billion tons per year

PHOTOSYNTHESIS
(60 billion tons per year)

RELEASED FROM SOIL BY MAN
2 billion tons per year

EARTH RESERVOIR

RELEASED FROM EARTH INTERIOR
100 million tons per year (volcanoes, etc.)

ATMOSPHERE

WEATHERING OF ROCKS
(100 million tons per year)

**Fossil Fuels
40,000 x 10⁹ tons**

COMBUSTION OF FUELS BY MAN
6 billion tons per year (2% motor vehicles)

**OCEANIC RESERVOIR
130,000 x 10⁹ tons**

OCEAN -- ATMOSPHERE EXCHANGE
100 billion tons per year

OCEAN -- ATMOPHERE EXCHANGE
100 billion tons per year

CARBON RELEASABLE FROM FOSSIL FUELS

RESOURCE	WORLD PRODUCTION IN 1967	REMAINING RESOURCES	CARBON ULTIMATELY RELEASABLE
Coal	115×10^9 tons	7270×10^9 tons	2250×10^9 tons
Petroleum	27×10^9 tons	1460×10^9 tons	244×10^9 tons
Natural gas	9.5×10^{12} cu. m.	864×10^{12} cu. m.	342×10^9 tons
Natural gas liquids	1.17×10^9 tons	121×10^9 tons	39×10^9 tons
Shale Oil	-------	481×10^9 tons	370×10^9 tons

biosphere and so stabilizing the internal temperature ranges.

It has been suggested that the increase of carbon dioxide in the atmosphere, due to our increased full usage patterns, may be affecting this greenhouse screening. The possibility of steadily raising average temperature ranges at the earth's surface has been discussed with their eventual gross effects in, for example, the reduction of the polar and other ice-cap areas.

It has been calculated that more than 100 million tons of fixed nitrogen in the form of ammonia and nitrates is annually transferred from the atmosphere to the surface of the earth as part of a natural precipitation process. In the United States alone there falls upon the face of our land annually more than 4 million tons of table salt, 2½ million tons of sodium sulphate, and 36 million tons of calcium compounds —all in rain water.[7]

The nitrogen cycle, one of the fundamental cycles in the biosphere, is being massively intruded upon by man: agriculture in the United States annually introduces about 7 million tons of nitrogen into the cycle, an amount roughly equal to the overall annual biological turnover of nitrogen.[8]

The energies used in the extraction, processing, transportation and use cycles of all the industrial materials are obtained mainly from burning the fossil fuels—oil, coal, natural gas. Each ton of these fuels that is used releases large amounts of carbon dioxide and other gases into the atmosphere. From 1860 to 1960, this has been calculated to have increased the atmosphere carbon dioxide concentration by 14 percent; during the eight years from 1954 to 1962, the average rate of increase was estimated at 5 percent.

. . . a ton of coal burned in a power plant where electricity is generated may emit from 2 to 9 kilograms of sulphur oxides, depending on the type of installation, 8 to 10 kilograms of nitrogen oxides and 10 to 20 kilograms of particulate matter if no control equipment is used. Under the same conditions an equal quantity of heat units in the form of residual oil would emit from 1.5 to 4.0 kilograms of sulphur oxides, 8 to 9 kilograms of nitrogen oxides and an insignificant amount of particulates. Natural gas, the cleanest of the fossil fuels, would generate only negligible amounts of particulates and sulphur oxides and about half the same amount of nitrogen oxides as an equivalent amount of coal.[9]

NATURAL AND MAN-MADE TRACE-GAS CYCLES
(in metric tons)

	NATURAL	MAN-MADE
OZONE	2×10^9	small
CARBON DIOXIDE	7×10^{10}	1.5×10^{10}
WATER	5×10^{14}	1×10^{10}
CARBON MONOXIDE	?	2×10^8
SULFUR	1.42×10^8	7.3×10^7
NITROGEN	1.4×10^9	1.5×10^7

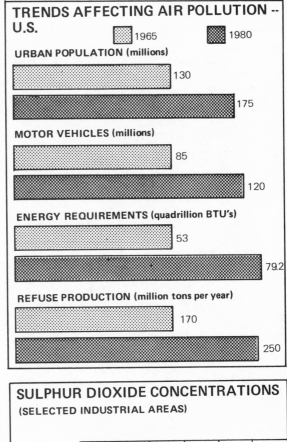

TRENDS AFFECTING AIR POLLUTION -- U.S.   1965   1980

URBAN POPULATION (millions)
130
175

MOTOR VEHICLES (millions)
85
120

ENERGY REQUIREMENTS (quadrillion BTU's)
53
79.2

REFUSE PRODUCTION (million tons per year)
170
250

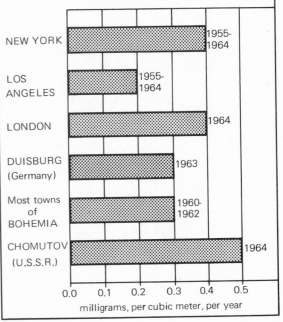

SULPHUR DIOXIDE CONCENTRATIONS
(SELECTED INDUSTRIAL AREAS)

NEW YORK — 1955-1964
LOS ANGELES — 1955-1964
LONDON — 1964
DUISBURG (Germany) — 1963
Most towns of BOHEMIA — 1960-1962
CHOMUTOV (U.S.S.R.) — 1964

0.0 0.1 0.2 0.3 0.4 0.5
milligrams, per cubic meter, per year

Over the past 100 years we have poured 360 million tons of CO_2 into the atmosphere. By the end of the century, this increase of 10 percent is likely to have risen to 25 percent and we shall have released enough CO_2 to raise the atmospheric temperature by two degrees centigrade via the greenhouse effect. It is suggested, however, that paradoxically, the increase of dust in the air reverses this trend, negating the increase in carbon dioxide.

Sulphur oxides, a more immediately harmful aerial pollutant in highly industrialized countries, is expected to show a 75 percent increase over present critical levels by 1980. A single, fossil-fuel, power-generating plant may emit several hundred tons of sulphur dioxide per day and, under certain weather conditions, locally overburden the air of a whole city. When this effect is increased by larger multiple fuel uses in dense urban concentrations, the results become lethally apparent in the number of people affected by respiratory diseases and, in certain cases, by the number of deaths attributable directly or indirectly to aerial pollution.

One of the prime contributors to urban pollution is the internal combustion engine, whose exhaust gases in the last 30 years have become a major source of air pollution. Associated with this source is the rise in lead pollution, which is a cumulative poison. Measurements indicate that there is ten times more lead in the atmosphere than 200 years ago; approximately 2.5 pounds of lead compounds per capita are voided into the atmosphere annually and this amount eventually goes into the soil and is taken up by plants, animals, and people. For example, large urban aggregates such as Los Angeles show an average concentration of lead in the air at 50 times that in rural areas.

The amount of air pollution from cars is more closely related to miles traveled, and particularly to urban miles traveled. In 1946, urban miles traveled were 170 billion. Twenty years later this had more than doubled, to 470 billion, and it is still rising. What this indicates is that our control efforts continue to lag behind our capacity to pollute the air.[10]

Each car on the road today exhausts between one-quarter to one-half ton of carbon monoxide and hydrocarbons a year.[11]

The costs of normal atmospheric pollution to each of the 200 million Americans is approximately $65 per year. To those in highly polluted areas cost per person in medical bills, household main-

	TONS OF POLLUTANTS EMITTED ANNUALLY—U.S.	
PERCENT	TYPE OF POLLUTANT	TONS ANNUALLY
53	MONOXIDE CARBON	72,000,000
18	SULFUR DIOXIDE	25,000,000
13	HYDROCARBONS	18,000,000
8	PARTICULATES	12,000,000
8	NITROGEN OXIDES	12,000,000
	TOTAL	139,000,000

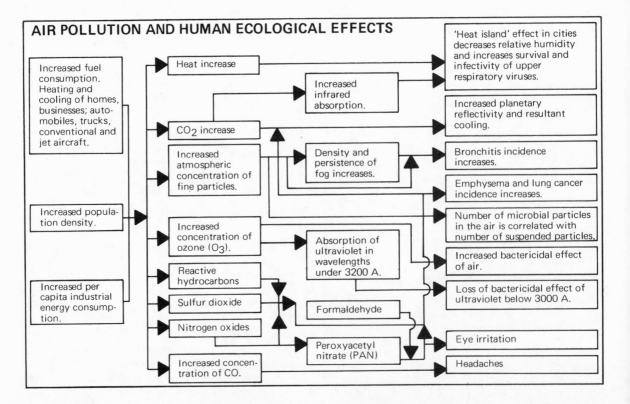

AIR POLLUTION AND HUMAN ECOLOGICAL EFFECTS

SOURCES OF AIR POLLUTION--U.S.
(In millions of tons annually--1960)

	Carbon monoxide	Sulphur oxides	Nitrogen oxides	Hydrocarbons	Particulate matter	TOTALS
Motor vehicles	66	1	6	12	1	86
Industry	2	9	2	4	6	23
Power plants	1	12	3	1	3	20
Space heating	2	3	1	1	1	8
Refuse disposal	1	1	1	1	1	5
TOTALS	72	26	13	19	12	

AUTOMOTIVE POLLUTION

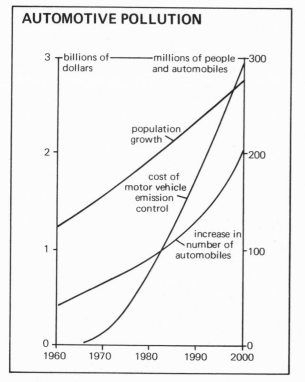

WORLD PRODUCTION OF FOSSIL FUELS AND CARBON DIOXIDE PRODUCED

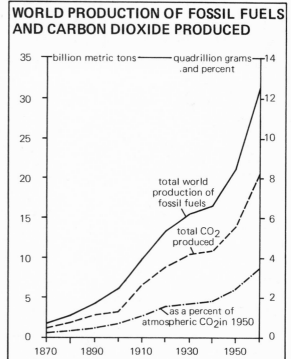

tenance, etc., can be more than $200 per year. The total cost to U.S. agriculture is more than $500 million per year.

Carbon monoxide and sulfur oxides, approximately 70 percent by weight of all air pollution, will probably account for 70 percent of the money spent on air pollution control. Estimates are that pollution control and rollback can cost the United States $4.1 billion per year for 15 years. Sulfur oxides and particulates from power plants and industrial installations account for 30 percent by weight of all air pollution; cost for a reduction of 65 to 70 percent of this amount would be $750 million per year.

So far, in the recent past, the bulk of our intrusions into the atmosphere have had directly negative effects and have been conducted with little regard for their immediate or long-range consequences. We have largely ignored, for example, the enormous potential energies inherent in the massive and constantly renewed energy circulation patterns in the atmospheric cycles. Wind power as used for centuries only gives access to the smallest fraction of such available energies. If we were to redirect some of our resources, now devoted to further extraction and use of our limited fossil fuels, toward the possibilities of "tapping in" more directly to the atmospheric energy potential, this might begin to provide a relatively massive supply of renewable and pollution-free energies.

TERRESTRIAL

The primary ecological habitat of human society is the land surface, from which the bulk of the food and other energies and materials necessary for its maintenance are extracted. Though the land area available constitutes about one quarter of the earth's surface, that portion well populated and intensively used is less than a quarter of the available land surface—the rest is desert, jungle, ice cap, mountain peaks, etc. As earlier noted, the populated areas also sustain large animal populations.

Usable agricultural land provides food through direct use af edible crops or through animal food converters. The world community presently depends for its food on about three percent of the earth's surface of arable crop land and about six percent of the forest lands. In terms of traditional food-yield practices, this area is further confined to a thin layer of topsoil, averaging 7 to 12 inches in depth, where most of the plant nutrients are present in a relatively critical distribution balance. The geological "building" of such topsoil layers is calculated to take about 7,000 years to deposit. It is, strictly speaking, a renewable but fragile resource base critically dependent on the various geochemical and climatic cycles. In recent historical time, however, the rapid growth of population, its aggregation in great densities, and the consequent pressure on the food soils have led to misuse and relatively permanent loss of great areas of this life-support base.

Recent calculations [12] suggest that the present maintenance of three billion humans in the biosphere requires a plant yield sufficient to accommodate 14.5 billion other consumers. These others, the animal populations, are an essential element in maintaining the humans by acting as intermediate processors for many products indigestible by man. For example, pigs consume as much as do 1,600 million people, when measured on a global scale; the world horse population has a protein intake corresponding to that of 650 million humans, that is, approximately the population of China.

In this sense, one of our most stringent human limits remains biological and terrestrial, since human society is still almost wholly dependent on the plant and animal food yield from a relatively fixed area of arable land.

The encroachment upon this arable land area by highways, dams, urban development, industrial installations, all the attendant practices of materials mining and energy extraction, etc., is not, as yet, in any balanced relation to the acquisition of new

CARBON MONOXIDE EMISSIONS—U.S.
(IN MILLIONS OF TONS PER YEAR)

SOURCE	CARBON MONOXIDE EMISSIONS	PERCENT OF TOTAL
TECHNOLOGICAL SOURCES		
FUEL COMBUSTION IN MOBILE SOURCES		
Motor vehicles	59.2	62.7
Aircraft	2.4	2.5
Vessels	0.3	0.3
Railroads	0.1	0.1
Non-highway use of fuels	1.8	1.9
FUEL COMBUSTION IN STATIONARY SOURCES		
Coal	0.8	0.8
Fuel oil	0.1	0.1
Natural gas	trace	trace
Wood	1.0	1.0
INDUSTRIAL PROCESSES	11.2	11.9
SOLID WASTE COMBUSTION	7.8	8.3
MISCELLANEOUS	9.7	10.3
	94.4	100.0
NATURAL SOURCES		
FOREST FIRES	7.2	

GLOBAL EMISSIONS OF CARBON MONOXIDE
(in millions of tons per year)

SOURCE	CONSUMPTION	CARBON MONOXIDE EMISSIONS
GASOLINE	379	193
COAL	3,074	12
WOOD	466	16
INCINERATION	500	25
FOREST FIRES	18 acres per year	11.3

arable lands, by desert, forest, and other reclamations. For example, in the United States alone, urbanization and transportation draws more than a million acres per year from cultivation. In terms of the overall ecological balance, we do not know whether such gross redistributions of land use and reclamation to arable purposes are indeed favorable. The agricultural revolution may have had, and continues to have, as disturbing an effect as industrialization.

Though the growth of population has been accompanied by more intensive cultivation and higher food yields per land unit, the amount of presently usable land per capita is declining. This decreasing amount of land per capita is, however, only a relative measure. The actual amount of land surface available and "relatively" unused may be gauged from the fact that the entire U.S. population occupies much less than ten percent of the continental land area. In relation to food yield, many more people may be fed off the land than on it via agricultural occupation.

Humanity's increasing mobility also suggests that fixed land habitation in specific locales may only be one of a number of alternative living patterns. Current pressures on recreational lands, however, suggest that we need to take a much longer and "multiple use" view of our land requirements. Even the so-called wilderness is no longer there to be conquered: it has become a rather fragile, easily disturbed component of our essential environmental balance.

Our rate of extraction, use, and redistribution of materials from the land has increased vastly in the past century: we now "consume" in various ways over 200 tons per capita as against approximately 50 tons per capita around the turn of the century. We need to recall, therefore, that most of the material resources contained within the land surface have been built up over long periods of geological time. The metal and mineral deposits upon which human society is dependent for its extended technological systems have taken millions of years to form and accumulate. A side glance at our present use rate of these non-renewable resources shows:

	GEOLOGICAL TIME REQUIRED TO PRODUCE 1 TON (millions of years)	MAN'S REMOVAL RATE (millions of tons per year)
PETROLEUM	250	600
COAL	1,000	2,000
IRON	2,000	200
LEAD	4,000	4

In the case of metals, though these are not renewable in the strictest sense, they may be successively reused as they are processed through successive use/scrap/reuse cycles. There is, of course, a variable intrinsic loss in each reuse cycle: in the case of steel scrap recycling, there is an approximate ten percent loss in each cycle. Such losses vary with different materials. Our fossil fuel extractions and uses are of a much more serious and directly depletive nature.

LAND AND WASTE MANAGEMENT. Any very large addition of arable land through conversion of deserts, jungle, or rain forest seems unlikely in the next three decades. It has been estimated, however, that to keep up with the current population

PROPORTION OF LAND USE: WORLD AND REGIONAL

	% arable land under permanent crop	% meadow and permanent pasture	% wasteland	% forestland
WORLD	11	19	40	30
AFRICA	9	21	45	25
U.S.S.R.	10	17	34	39
NORTH AMERICA	10	13	42	35
LATIN AMERICA	5	20	27	48
SOUTH ASIA	22	13	40	25
EAST ASIA	10	15	63	12
OCEANIA	4	54	33	9
EUROPE	31	18	23	28

PER CAPITA USE OF SELECTED FUELS, COPPER, AND AGRICULTURAL MINERALS

	USE PER PERSON PER YEAR (WORLD POPULATION)				
	PETROLEUM (barrels)	NATURAL GAS (cubic feet)	COPPER (pounds)	PHOSPHATE ROCK (pounds)	POTASH (pounds KO_2)
1910	.19	—	1.15	7.1	—
1920	.38	—	1.16	8.3	1.47
1930	.70	1060	1.70	12.8	2.48
1940	.96	1360	2.20	8.4	2.73
1950	1.52	2780	2.80	20.1	4.5
1960	2.62	5700	3.76	30.2	7.1

increase we will need 30 to 40 million new acres, or a food production equivalent, each year. This also begs the question of required improvements in overall nutritional balance in both the lesser developed and overdeveloped world regions.

Increasing crop yields through new strains of high-yield grains has already increased our time margin, but is possibly only of limited and short-range help. Strategies in this area tend to increase dependence on agricultural ties to existing land-use patterns, and require increases in the backup systems of pest control, fertilizer, and so forth.

Fertilizer alone is calculated to require approximately a 30 percent increase in overall world terms to attain food production adequacy. But almost 500 million people already depend on high chemical fertilized land; to accommodate an additional three billion in these terms in 30 years may be impractical.

We often tend to forget the linkages and second order consequences here. In making "artificial" fertilizers and other soil nutrients to make the land more productive, we also, indirectly, destroy crops through by-products of the increased industrial activities used to provide more efficient agricultural usage. Each calorie of food produced in highly mechanized agriculture requires roughly an equivalent calorie of fuel to power tractors, harvesters, processing, and transportation. Such fuels are mainly the fossil fuels—which contribute to the aerial pollutants which directly and indirectly decrease crop yield. In addition, to make each ton of nitrogenous fertilizer, we use in direct and related industrial practice, one million tons of steel and five million tons of coal or fuel equivalent.

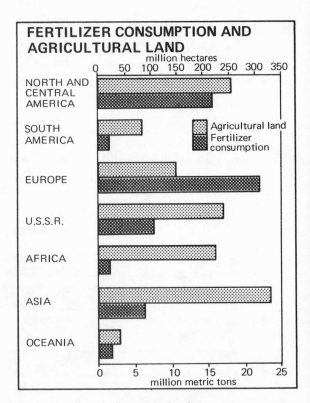

FERTILIZER CONSUMPTION AND AGRICULTURAL LAND

These effect linkages and adverse consequences are often tenuous and so indirectly related that they remain concealed until they reach dangerous proportions; e.g., the DDT spread on a bean field may destroy a nearby hive of honey bees, and thereby prevent pollination of a fruit orchard a half-mile away, raising the price of fruit 50 miles away. Such micro-examples may be found in multiple

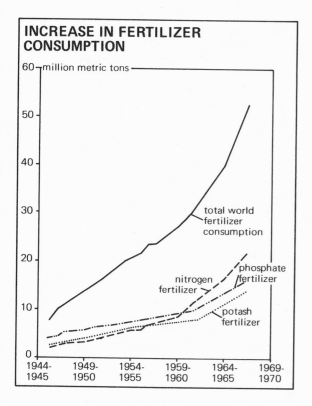

INCREASE IN FERTILIZER CONSUMPTION

60 million metric tons

total world fertilizer consumption

phosphate fertilizer

nitrogen fertilizer

potash fertilizer

ENVIRONMENTAL EFFECTS
DEFOLIATION AND CROP DESTRUCTION—VIETNAM

ACRES SPRAYED PER YEAR

YEAR	DEFOLIATION	CROP DESTRUCTION	TOTAL
1962	17,119	717	17,836
1963	34,517	297	34,814
1964	53,873	10,136	64,009
1965	94,726	49,637	144,363
1966	775,894	112,678	888,572
1967	1,486,446	221,312	1,707,758
1968	1,297,244	87,064	1,384,308

BIOLOGICAL MAGNIFICATION OF DDT

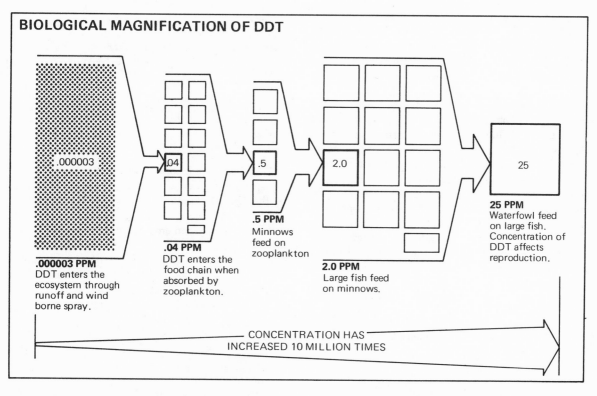

.000003

.04

.5

2.0

25

.000003 PPM
DDT enters the ecosystem through runoff and wind borne spray.

.04 PPM
DDT enters the food chain when absorbed by zooplankton.

.5 PPM
Minnows feed on zooplankton

2.0 PPM
Large fish feed on minnows.

25 PPM
Waterfowl feed on large fish. Concentration of DDT affects reproduction.

CONCENTRATION HAS INCREASED 10 MILLION TIMES

forms in many other sectors of our agri-industrial undertakings. DDT, because of its cumulative nature and recent emergence into public view, is a convenient indicator of a chemical weapon against pests, the original estimates of whose immediate and extremely valuable benefits did not include due investment into assessing the deleterious, long-term and large-scale consequences. So far we have re-leased about 1,000 million pounds into the environment, and continue to use over 100 million pounds per year with a total world annual production of 1,300 million pounds. The chain of its successive concentration in the food cycle is only now partially established after many years of use and its larger consequential effects are only now being measured; e.g., minute amounts have been found to reduce photosynthesis in marine plants by as much as 75 percent. Similar questioning now goes on about other products such as mercury, lead, etc., whose large-scale introduction and use has not been adequately conceptualized or monitored.

> The publicity given to the pollution problems caused by the DDT compounds in the environment has tended to minimize the threat of other environmental pollutants. DDT is produced in smaller quantities than many industrial products. The most abundant synthetic pollutants in the environment, after the DDT compounds, may be a class of chemicals called polychlorinated biphenols, or PCB. They are used in such vast amounts in industry that they can be purchased in railway car quantities . . . the usefulness of the polychlorinated biphenols to industry derives to a large part from their chemical stability and their misability with oil and other non-polar substances. The same properties ensure that they will not dissolve in water, that they will readily enter biological systems and be concentrated in food chains, and that they can be degraded, if at all, only with great difficulty by biological systems . . . they are now found world wide in marine fish and birds, and in human mother's milk. . . . Tolerance limits for these compounds have not been established and the tests for carcinogenicity, effects on reproduction, etc., have not yet been done.[13]

Although the problems of environmental pollutants and wastes are generally laid to increased industrial usage, we may note that, in the United States alone, more than a billion tons of agricultural wastes are produced annually. Only a fraction of this is recycled. In terms of animal wastes, analysts have noted that there is a largely unrecognized problem: disposal facilities to cope with animal wastes from highly concentrated feedlot operations do not exist. In one U.S. state, which has as many pigs and cattle as people (approximately four million), the animal population is estimated to produce sewage and other wastes equivalent to ten times the human population. To this aspect of environmental imbalance related to intensive agricultural practices, we may add the growing incidence of fertilizer, pesticide, and other chemical run-offs that contribute to the deterioration of the water systems.

> Putting all pollutants into the same units—millions of tons—is somewhat misleading. Some pollutants are harmful even in very small amounts. Some are more harmful than others, and some are more harmful together than separately.[14]

Traditional agricultural practice, even where mechanized and supposedly advanced, remains largely a one-way "open" system of exclusive and competing market-oriented interests. The only realistic and long-term solutions lie in the redesign of our whole food production system: through a more integrated and ecological approach which treats the agri-industry, food processing, and distribution system as a unitary system.

Other "off the land" directions which may augment our food supply via the production of artificial protein, food additives, and food synthesis through microbial and other systems, as well as increasing marine food yields, may eventually provide viable alternative directions to current practices. Taken together in various combinations, these approaches do offer the promise of solving the world's food problem. To be effective in time, however, they may require development on a global scale with capabilities and expenditures approaching that of the combined space programs of the United States and the Soviet Union. Present overall expenditures in this vital area of "survival research and development" do not amount, in world total, to one day's expenditure in our current wars and associated defense programs.

Waste disposal, in general, even in the most advanced countries, is still archaic. Methods used in our larger urban concentrations are little improved from the traditional systems evolved for much smaller and less waste-productive communities of the preindustrial period. The average city of a half million people now disposes of 50 million gallons of sewage daily and produces solid wastes of about eight pounds per person per day.

> Pollutants are the residues of things we make use of once and throw away. . . . As the earth becomes more crowded there is no longer an "away" . . . our whole economy is based on taking natural resources, converting them into things that are consumer products, selling them to consumers and then forgetting about them. But there are no consumers—only users. The user employs the product, sometimes changes it in form, but he does not consume he just discards it. . . . One person's trash basket is another person's living space." [15]

An urban population of one million needs dumping space for 5,000 cubic feet of refuse each day. In the United States, household wastes amount to approximately 190 million tons annually. Combined with industrial, commercial, and agricultural wastes, this comes to 3.5 billion tons, including 7 million junked autos, 20 million tons of paper, 48 million cans, 26,000 million bottles and jars, 3,000 million tons of waste rock and mill tailings, and 142 million tons of smoke and noxious fumes.

> We throw away 3.5 billion tons of solid wastes per year: 360 million tons of this are household, municipal and industrial wastes; 2 billion tons are agricultural wastes: 1.1 billion tons are mineral wastes.[16]
> . . . the total expenditures for collection of trash and other solid wastes . . . are approximately $4.5 billion per year. . . . Collection of solid wastes . . . amounts to 190 million tons per year (5.3 pounds per person per day). By 1980, the amount collected . . . is expected to be over 340 million tons/year (8 pounds per person per day).[17]

Little progress may be made in this area of waste management until we have drastically altered our concept of waste. Instead of thinking about how we can "get rid of" our discards and residues—by burying, burning and dumping them as "innocuously" as possible—we need to reconceptualize our whole process of the use of our resources.

A pound of bacteria, feeding on crude oil so worthless that it is burned as waste, can grow fast enough to produce 10 pounds of protein in a day. If a yearling calf were able to manufacture protein at the same rate, it would end the day roughly the size of a three-car garage and it would have consumed several tons of expensive grain in the process. The cost of protein produced from waste effluents is approaching 3 cents/pound, compared with agriculture and animal protein at 10 cents/pound. Algae produces protein at a rate of 30 to 50 tons/acre/

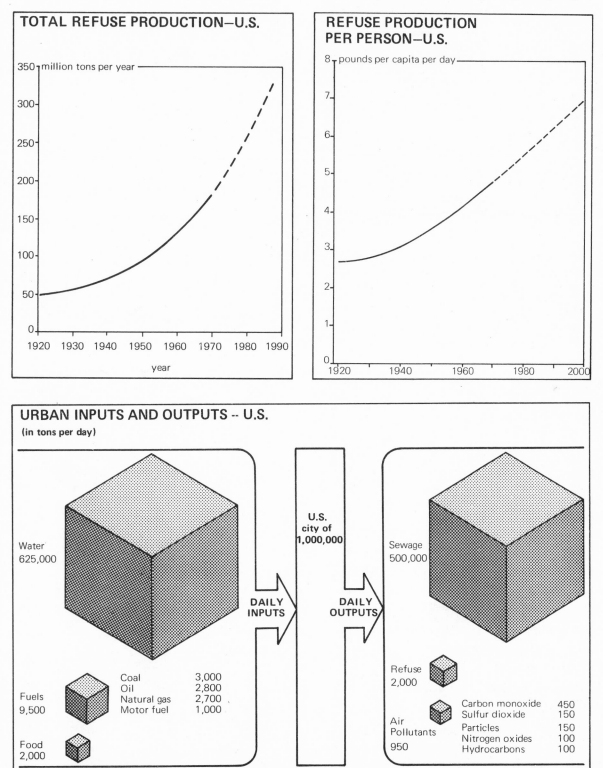

TOTAL REFUSE PRODUCTION—U.S.

350 million tons per year

year

REFUSE PRODUCTION PER PERSON—U.S.

8 pounds per capita per day

URBAN INPUTS AND OUTPUTS -- U.S.

(in tons per day)

Water 625,000

Fuels 9,500

Coal	3,000
Oil	2,800
Natural gas	2,700
Motor fuel	1,000

Food 2,000

DAILY INPUTS

U.S. city of 1,000,000

DAILY OUTPUTS

Sewage 500,000

Refuse 2,000

Air Pollutants 950

Carbon monoxide	450
Sulfur dioxide	150
Particles	150
Nitrogen oxides	100
Hydrocarbons	100

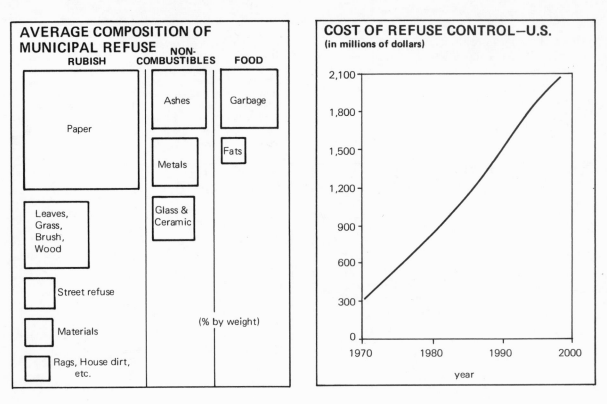

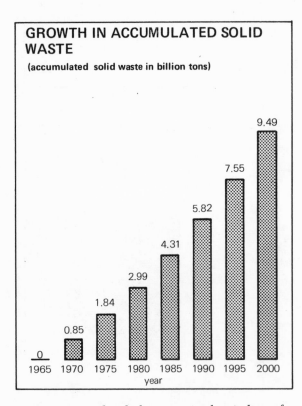

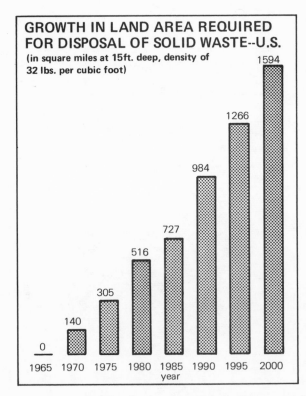

year, compared with the conventional agriculture of 3 to 5/tons/acre/year.[18]

The useless discards, residues, and pollutants from one process may be valuable raw materials and nutrients of another. Our junked autos and other metallic discards are, indeed, "surface mines" or man-made reservoirs of metals which we need to conserve and draw upon for further use and reuse cycles. We need to elaborate this whole system's approach to the ecological redesign of all of our human systems—industrial, agriculture, urban, etc.—so that their various parts function in more directly symbiotic relationships.

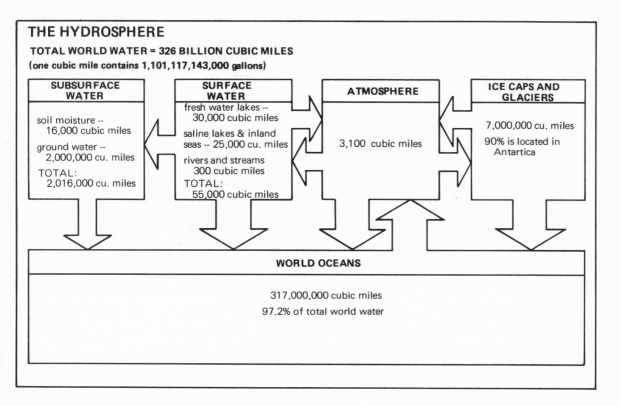

THE HYDROSPHERE

TOTAL WORLD WATER = 326 BILLION CUBIC MILES
(one cubic mile contains 1,101,117,143,000 gallons)

SUBSURFACE WATER	SURFACE WATER	ATMOSPHERE	ICE CAPS AND GLACIERS
soil moisture -- 16,000 cubic miles ground water -- 2,000,000 cu. miles TOTAL: 2,016,000 cu. miles	fresh water lakes -- 30,000 cubic miles saline lakes & inland seas -- 25,000 cu. miles rivers and streams 300 cubic miles TOTAL: 55,000 cubic miles	3,100 cubic miles	7,000,000 cu. miles 90% is located in Antartica

WORLD OCEANS

317,000,000 cubic miles

97.2% of total world water

It might prompt us (also) to examine other "economies" we seek at the expense of the environment. Radioactive products seep from nuclear reactors because trapping them would "prohibitively" raise the cost of the electricity generated. Mountains and the forests they support are devastated by strip mining to keep costs of extraction low. Urban sprawl consumes acreage wholesale because land is valued in terms not of its role in the environment but of its market price.[19]

The negative costs now inherent in our "piecemeal and open-ended" series of unrelated and uncoordinated activities may then be reversed toward positive gains in the more economic use of increasingly precious raw materials, in the multiple uses of energy inputs and outputs and in the directly visible gains in the quality of our environment.

MARINE

The marine environ covers more than 70 percent of surface. In terms of space, food, and other potential resources, this is like having several more environments at human disposal. The comparatively shallow areas of the continental shelf alone, are in area about half that of the earth lowlands where most of humanity lives. The biomass productivity in these marine, coastal-shelf regions is also about twice as great as that of the major ocean areas: The coastal regions and upswelling zones are much more productive than the open sea and an area approximately as large as California produces about half of the world's fish supply.

Our knowledge of the oceans, however, is rudimentary. Barely one percent of all sea organisms have been studied and few of the cyclic migrations of its larger creatures have been charted. About four-fifths of the planet's animal life and the bulk of its vegetation are underwater but comparatively little of this is used as food.

Much play has been made of the ocean's "inner space" as our next great exploratory frontier. The volume and expanse, and the richness and variety of life of the seas and oceans certainly encourages such optimism. The main critical difficulty, again, may be to regulate their exploration and use now on a comprehensive enough scale before unrestricted exploitation, industrial, and military misusage render them unfit even to sustain their own organic populations.

The idea of the seas as a vast and relatively inexhaustible reservoir of resources needs to be tempered by some realization of the extent to which we already use its food and other resources and the extent to which we may already be interfering in major ways with the cyclical replenishment of these resources.

Considerable spoilage of the oceans has already occurred in many regions, particularly the key coastal shelves. Indiscriminate dumping of sewage and industrial wastes has already ruined the potential use of many such areas for some time to come. This spoilage has been further increased by the discharge and "spills" from tankers and ocean-drilling rigs which contaminate the waters and beaches for years and wreak heavy tolls of sea birds and other organ-

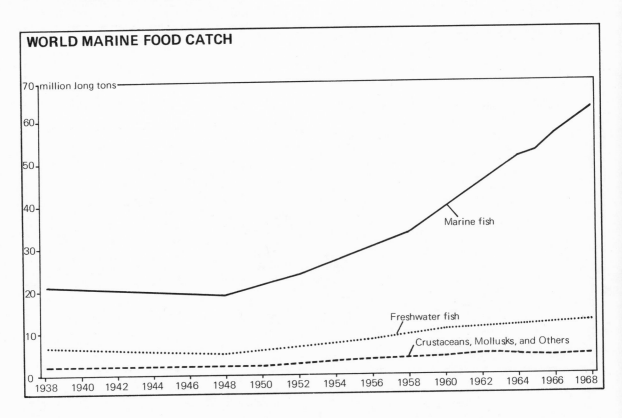

WORLD MARINE FOOD CATCH

isms. Old sea-mine fields still render large areas of the coastal waters unsafe, and are now accompanied by new hazards such as radioactive waste disposal and obsolete chemical and biological warfare compounds. Over fishing and hunting has led not only to greatly reduced catches, but also to the near extinction of many ocean species.

A mapping of the oil and other exploitation leases already operative on the shallow continental shelves around the world is an instructive forewarning that our so-called "inner space" frontier is no longer an open option for the world community, but that much of its potential use has already been foreclosed by various short-range commercial and other interests.

Of central importance to human purposes in the biosphere is the amount of food protein derived from the world fish catch. The total world fish harvest has been increased by about one-third since 1950, and the marine fisheries industry is now expanding faster than human population growth but the catch capacity of the industry and its capacities for future growth in terms of current practices is limited and measurably finite.

Already the fisheries for cod, herring, haddock, ocean perch, plaice, and other species in many areas of the North Atlantic are either operating at full capacity or are overexploited. Increased effort no longer yields an increased catch. The anchovy fishery in Peru, which now produces about ten million tons of fish per year, that is reduced to two million tons of fish meal, is now operating at full capacity.[20]

We may note, in passing, that the bulk of such fishmeal, high in protein, is exported from those areas in the lesser developed countries, whose con-

sumption of animal protein is far below the minimal desirable levels, to feed livestock and pets in the high protein advanced regions!

In the century from 1850 to 1950 the world catch increased tenfold—an average rate of about 25 percent per decade. In the next decade it nearly doubled, and this rapid growth is continuing. This increase has been accompanied by a changing pat-

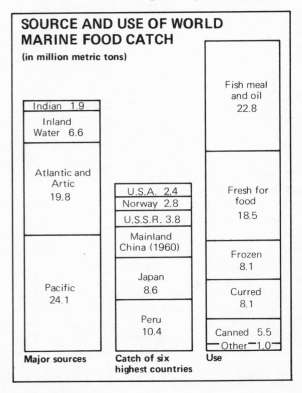

SOURCE AND USE OF WORLD MARINE FOOD CATCH
(in million metric tons)

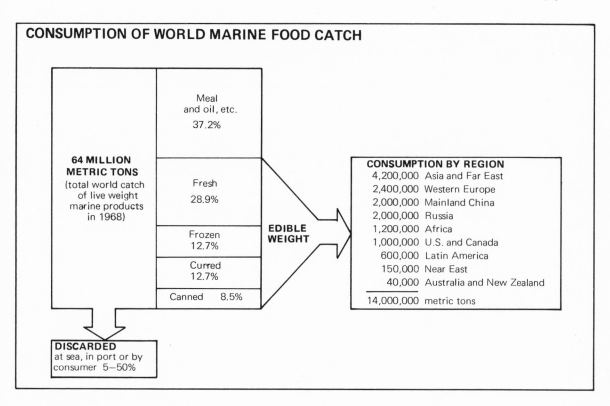

CONSUMPTION OF WORLD MARINE FOOD CATCH

64 MILLION METRIC TONS (total world catch of live weight marine products in 1968)

Meal and oil, etc. 37.2%

Fresh 28.9%

Frozen 12.7%

Curred 12.7%

Canned 8.5%

EDIBLE WEIGHT

CONSUMPTION BY REGION

4,200,000	Asia and Far East
2,400,000	Western Europe
2,000,000	Mainland China
2,000,000	Russia
1,200,000	Africa
1,000,000	U.S. and Canada
600,000	Latin America
150,000	Near East
40,000	Australia and New Zealand
14,000,000	metric tons

DISCARDED at sea, in port or by consumer 5–50%

tern of use . . . the trend has been for less of the catch to be used directly as human food and for more to be reduced to meal for animal feed. Just before World War II less than 10 percent of the world catch was turned into meal; by 1967 half of it was so used.[21]

Marine food resources, though finite, could be so managed as to provide a significantly increased contribution to diet adequacy for the world's hungry populations. Protein rich food additives have already been developed from fishmeals which can be used to correct widespread protein deficient diets. The technology of mariculture, of the "artificial" cultivation of shellfish and other edible organisms, and of sea farming, already promises a significantly higher yield than may be afforded by current practices. These enhanced uses of the oceans and coastal water are critical to our survival in the next few decades. Against them, we may note already that large amounts of fish taken in both inland and ocean waters have been condemned for human consumption due to high concentrations of DDT, mercury, and other toxins.

Human society has more than doubled the amount of mercury which ends up in oceans. Man annually sends 4,000 to 5,000 tons of this toxic pollutant into the oceans, compared to 4,000 tons introduced naturally into oceans through weathering processes. The U.S. uses 27 percent of the annual world production of mercury—9,200 metric tons. The U.S. produces only 10 percent, or 920 metric tons, however, and must acquire the rest.[22]

Ocean oil pollution has now reached critical proportions and its frequency and scale of occurrence

increases rapidly. In 1968, more than 500 major oil pipeline leaks were officialy reported averaging between 1,000 and 12,000 gallons per leak. Reliable international information suggests that an estimated 500,000 tons of crude oil—leaked or deliberately dumped—pollute the seas around the world annually. [23] At least 60 percent of the world's oil production is now transported by ocean tanker and as such transportation will increase particularly through more hazardous waters and in increasingly larger tanker units, there will be a concomitant rise in the amounts of leakages and spills.

The immediate, short-term effects of oil pollution are obvious and well understood in kind if not in extent. The coastal fouling and damage to bird populations has been documented abundantly . . . fouling on the high seas is just now being recognized, even though the amount of tar at the sea surface already exceeds the amount of surface plant life . . . (and) . . . we are rather ignorant about long-term and low-level effects of crude pollution.

In combination, the great complexity of the marine food chain and the stability of the hydrocarbons in marine organisms lead to a potentially dangerous situation. Once assimilated, this oil passes through the marine food chain, and eventually reaches organisms that are harvested for human consumption. One consequence will be the incorporation into food of materials which produce an undesirable flavor. A far more serious effect is the potential accumulation in human food of long-term poisons derived from crude oil, for instance, of carcinogenic compounds. Another concern is the possible long-term damage by pollution to the marine ecology . . . if we do not take care of the present biological resources in the sea, we may do irreversible damage to many marine organisms, to the marine food chain and we may eventually destroy the yield and the value of the food which we hope to recover from the sea.[24]

Mineral resource exploitation of the oceans is already in an advanced stage of development in both the extraction of sea-water elements and in the direct mining of metals and minerals from the ocean floor. The world's rivers now wash into the seas some four billion tons of dissolved inorganic matter and about five times as much undissolved materials. The dissolved constituents include such amounts of important chemical elements as 3.5 million tons of phosphorus, 100 million tons of potassium, and 10 million tons of fixed nitrogen.

In this regard, it has been estimated that in the United States some 200 tons of copper, in various forms, are lost in sewage annually for each million people, together with 50 tons each of such metals as manganese, lead, aluminum, and titanium. As many estuarine and coastal marine organisms specifically concentrate such minerals in their tissues as part of their ongoing metabolism, such naturally occurring agents could possibly be put into designed use as processing systems for such mineral concentration and recovery. Our domesticated land food plants and animals are precisely such an ongoing system for intermediate processing and concentration of specific food energies and materials.

WATER RESOURCES. Water, a key resource in daily life, agriculture, and industry is in critical balance in many world regions. Approximately 95 percent of the fresh waters are presently used at a greater rate than their precipitation replacement in ground surface waters.

Though much water use is of a multi-purpose "cycling" nature, and, therefore, differs from the more single use/discard patterns of other resources, the bulk increases in each use now begin to strain the storage, replenishment, and natural recycling capacities of many areas.

Population growth and urban concentration have been considerable factors of increase. Between 1900 and 1960 the amount of water used in cities increased more than seven times. By 1980 it is expected to be 12 times the 1900 level. In the United States, consumption has risen from 40 billion gallons per day in 1900 to over 300 billions gallons in the 1960s. The average Western per capita use is 150 gallons each day. Industry uses vast quantities of process water, including:

7-25 gallons to produce 1 gallon of gasoline
25,000 gallons to produce 1 ton of steel
50,000 gallons to produce 1 ton of paper
250,000 gallons to produce 1 ton of acetate

Agriculture still accounts for 10 percent of all usage, requiring 400 to 500 pounds of water for each pound of dry plant produce. The water to specific crop-ratio varies considerably.

The water courses of rivers, streams, and lakes have been grossly affected, not only from the sewage disposal of the cities and industrial wastes, but from intensified agricultural practices. Large amounts of soil additives, fertilizers, and chemical nutrients are washed off the lands through rainfall, irrigation, and drainage into the natural water courses where they disturb the aquatic life balances. The undue growth

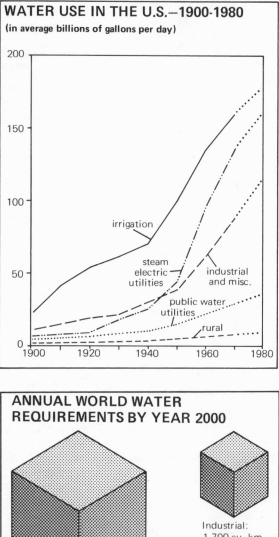

WATER USE IN THE U.S.—1900-1980
(in average billions of gallons per day)

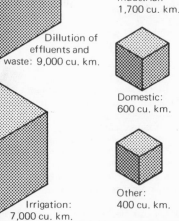

ANNUAL WORLD WATER REQUIREMENTS BY YEAR 2000

Dillution of effluents and waste: 9,000 cu. km.

Irrigation: 7,000 cu. km.

Industrial: 1,700 cu. km.

Domestic: 600 cu. km.

Other: 400 cu. km.

of algae and other plants decreases the oxygen supply for fish and other organisms thus attenuating the self-renewal of the water system. Such problems are not localized. In the case of pesticide runoffs and other toxic agents, introduced into upper river reaches, their concentrated effects may only be felt thousands of miles away.

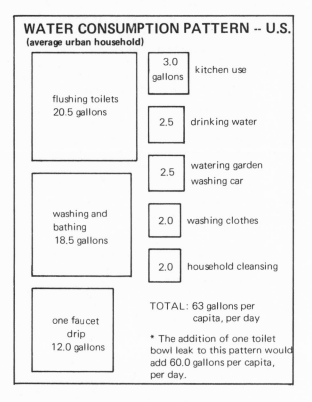

WATER CONSUMPTION PATTERN -- U.S.
(average urban household)

	gallons	
flushing toilets 20.5 gallons	3.0 gallons	kitchen use
	2.5	drinking water
	2.5	watering garden washing car
washing and bathing 18.5 gallons	2.0	washing clothes
	2.0	household cleansing
one faucet drip 12.0 gallons		

TOTAL: 63 gallons per capita, per day

* The addition of one toilet bowl leak to this pattern would add 60.0 gallons per capita, per day.

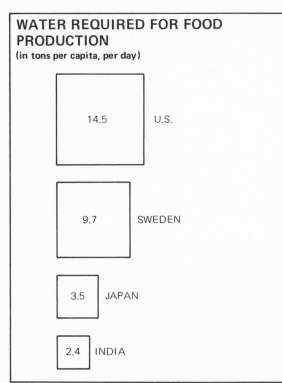

WATER REQUIRED FOR FOOD PRODUCTION
(in tons per capita, per day)

14.5	U.S.
9.7	SWEDEN
3.5	JAPAN
2.4	INDIA

Approximately 8 million people drink water with a bacteriological content that exceeds the limits of the U.S. Public Health Service Drinking Water Standards. . . . Nearly half of our 20,000 community water supply systems contain defects that are serious enough to place them in a potentially unsafe status.[25]

A major use of industrial water is as a coolant. For each kilowatt generated in a modern coal-fired power plant, approximately 6,000 Btu's of heat must be dissipated via cooling water through heat exchangers. Nuclear reactors are less efficient, requiring the dissipation of 1,000 Btu's per kilowatt hour generated. By 1980, the electrical power industry will require 200 billion gallons of water per day for cooling purposes. This water has great potential in the production of food through development of agriculture and enhancement of biological life. Thermal energy can increase the growth rate of the lower forms of marine life to provide additional food for the higher forms.[26]

The vastly increased number of uses of water by both agriculture and industry already indicates the possibility of critical shortages of this key resource. Water is being withdrawn for use at a faster rate than its return to the streams, lakes, rivers, and other sources by precipitation. In the more densely populated areas also requiring intensive irrigation, water supply is increasingly balanced by recourse to deeper drilling and "mining" of supplies from the stored water tables that have accumulated underground.

Much needs to be done to replenish and reuse the waters extracted by both agriculture and industry and to ensure that they are "returned to source" unpolluted by wastes, soil run-offs, and thermal discharges. So far such waters have been treated as a "free good" to be drawn upon prodigally as required, but in the next decades this cannot be tolerated.

The American people who used 40 billion gallons of water a day in 1900 and now use 350 billion gallons, will probably require between 700 and 1,000 billion gallons by the year 2000. Yet Congress found in 1963 that even with "optimum foreseeable developments in purification and engineering," not more than 650 billion gallons a day could be made available.[27]

SALT WATER IRRIGATION. The use of ocean waters for direct irrigation of the land has also been considerably pioneered in recent years. Specifically applicable to sandy, desert soils, such research is of extreme importance in the critical area of world food production.

Arid and semi-arid regions cover a third of the land's surface . . . many of (these) sandy regions could be made productive with salt water irrigation . . . any advance in making sandy soils productive adds to the resources available for the production of food. And any such addition can be a factor in the effort to keep the production of food abreast of the growth of population.[28]

DESALINATION. The production of fresh water from sea water is another growing use of the oceans.

The most promising developments are those combining nuclear power/fresh water generation plants in the same productive units. Such units in present use around the world have a desalting capacity of about 50 million gallons per day—an increase of 100 percent over the past two years.

It has been estimated that in 30 years time, approximately two billion human beings will obtain their fresh water from the sea in this manner. The cost of such converson from salt to fresh water has been steadily reduced:

$5 per 1000 gallons 12 years ago
$2 per 1000 gallons 4 years ago
$1 per 1000 gallions in 1966 [29]

The mineral by-products from such desalination plants are considerable and when their extraction is taken into consideration on a larger scale and by more efficient means, the cost per unit of fresh water supply would be increasingly offset.

It is unlikely, however, that these measures—direct irrigation by saline waters, desalination, etc.—taken alone will be sufficient in themselves to provide the quantity of water for use and reuse which will be required in the next 30 years. The amounts of energy and materials required to conduct such processing on a large enough scale to offset irrigation and other large uses directly are, for example, an important consideration. Our only overall strategy must include recasting and revising our present water-use practices and, where necessary and essential, redesigning those industrial and agricultural processes which "over use" this critical resource.

POLLUTION—NATURAL AND HUMAN. It is necessary to redress, in part, the semantic bias on "pollutants, garbage, and poisons." This usually tends to suggest vast quantities of alien substances being injected into an otherwise perfectly functioning system.

Man is perceived as the enemy, science and technology as the evil instruments which rape unsullied and fair nature. This over-emphatic "Mr. Clean" syndrome, a latter-day version of the Puritan ethic, is too obvious to require elaboration here. It does, however, decrease our awareness and appreciation of the degree to which technology has made nature more accessible and more enjoyable to man today—unlike the majority of men in the preindustrial period, when nature was viewed as a capricious and often cruel aspect of human struggle for survival.

Pollutants are as we perceive and designate them. Poisons are natural substances "out of place," or in excess of tolerable levels. The dust and gases of forest fires, volcanic ashes, pollens, marsh effluents, and so forth, are all "natural" pollutants of our natural environments.

We tend to forget the extent to which nature destroys—and pollutes—segments of itself, sporadically and violently—with man often a major victim in these upheavals. Among the greatest of these were: the earthquake in Shensi Province of China in 1556, killing an estimated 800,000 people . . . the volcanic eruption of 1470 B.C. that destroyed the Minoan civilization . . . the great flood of the Hwang-ho River in 1887 that swept 900,000 people to their death; the famine in India in 1770 that claimed the lives of a third of this country's population—tens of millions of people; and the 1877-78 famine in China that killed 9,500,000. And centuries before man seriously tampered with nature through modern medicine, between 1347 and 1351, the Black Death (bubonic plague) wiped out 75,000,000 people in Europe. History records numerous other types of plagues and natural disasters that have periodically destroyed various forms of life and changed the face of the earth . . . long before man and his new technology interfered with the balance of nature.[30]

Our concern here is to appraise more fully the role of man-made systems which are also natural systems in the overall functioning of the ecological context.

HUMAN SYSTEMS

Humanity and its "systems," social organizations, institutional arrangements, and so forth, should be regarded as a wholly integral process. We become accustomed, for various analytical and practically oriented conveniences, to isolating some feature of this process and considering it as representative of the whole.

As in dealing with the different sectors of the physical environment, we need to remind ourselves constantly that this differentiation and classification into parts and subsystems is a conceptual device only. Even our larger divisions such as the economy, the polity, the family, etc., are often no more than a labeling convenience for some specific aspect of human activity which in the end analysis must be related back to its place in the overall human process.

The use of the term "system" requires particular vigilance in this regard. The complexity and variety of interactive relations within human activities often force us back to simplistic models—particularly for measurement and accounting procedures. We tend to rely heavily on "administratively convenient" models and data. This is also evident, for example, in the present compilation of "facts and trends" which are overly biased on those quantitative measures which have been accumulated.

Though our analytical schema may function well as limited conceptual supports and may aid in reducing complexity within more manageable disciplinary formats, they often lead us toward overly mechanical models such as economic man, technological man, behavioral man, and so on. Such concepts, abstracted for convenience, tend to become "reified," i.e., they assume an autonomous reality in and of themselves. The partial aspect becomes accepted as explicable of the whole's behavior. This is particularly dangerous when we attempt to deal with human problems in such reified terms. We all too often assume that many large-scale human problems may be solved within artifical divisions and partial models set up for intellectual convenience.

Our present schema in which the overall ecosystem relations are labeled in their various divisions should also be treated as an extremely limited conceptual aid. Its linearly connected relationships can in no way approximate the dynamic complexity of even its smallest subsystems' units.

Again, no social problem of small or large scale—and all human problems are axiomatically social—may be solved within the terms or models of any single field or discipline. A wholly technological, economic, or biological solution, however logical and efficient, may fail completely by overlooking some apparent, but minor, sociocultural requirement.

The divisions used here—biophysical, psychosocial, technological—are therefore adopted for present convenience. They overlap considerably, and are in no way suggested as an exhaustive classification of the major aspects of human activities in the biosphere.

BIOPHYSICAL

The basic biophysical functions which we share with many other organism only furnish some of the parameters of our ecosystem requirements. Our distinctive human needs are complicated by the high degree of social development of the human species. Social patterns are more determinant of biophysical events than we generally concede.

There are few specific biological and physical requirements which give human beings any uniqueness as a life form. As with most other organisms, the biophysical requirements for the optimal maintenance of human life fall within a relatively narrow and specific range. The basic energy process is that of consuming food energies in combination with the oxidation process in respiration.

Air, water, and food, within various degrees of temperature and pressure, are the key requirements. Individuals' daily needs vary with age, weight, health, activity, etc. (Figures given below are for an average male adult.)

Oxygen intake need per day is approximately 1.35 pounds under normal conditions. About 2.2 pounds of carbon dioxide are exhaled. This is largely taken up by plants and reconverted into oxygen and food in the photosynthesis cycle.

The need for water is more stringent than the need for food. The daily water need is approximately five pounds per day.

The body can lose practically all stored animal starch or glycogen, all reserves of fat and about one-half of the protein which is stored or built into structures, and not be confronted with great danger. But the loss of 10 percent of body water is serious and a loss of 20 to 22 percent means certain death.[31]

Depending on cultural context, much larger quantities are used for various other physiological functions, such as washing, general hygiene, etc.

Man has a narrow physiological adjustment to temperature variability. He is, in this sense, a "subtropical" animal functioning best where 24 hour temperatures average between 63 to 73 degrees Fahrenheit. Pressure is also a limited adjustment area for the human organism and may be noted particularly in physiological difficulties of high altitude or underwater work.

Sleep varies directly with age more markedly, perhaps, than other requirements in relation to body size, etc. From 18 to 20 hours per day when newborn, the need declines through 12 to 14 hours in the growing child, 7 to 9 hours for the mature adult and thence to 5 to 7 in later ages.

Noise tolerance is also critical. Some comparative measures are as follows:

Normal conversation	60 Decibels
Urban street noise	80
Well amplified discoteque band	120
Low-flying jet air craft	130
Threshhold of pain	140

Prolonged exposure to high-level noises (about 90 decibels or so) can impair the ability of the ear to detect certain weak auditory signals, temporarily or sometimes on a permanent basis. A minimum of six million and perhaps as many as 16 million industrial workers are threatened with degrees of loss of hearing from exposure to noise on the job. Prolonged exposure to noises above 80 decibels (roughly the loudness of an ordinary alarm clock) can produce some permanent shift in auditory threshold. This partial deafness is also accompanied by a lessened efficiency and reduction of eye movement and ability to focus. At sustained 120 decibels (less than that experienced by a riveter) noise has been found to impair equilibrium. Noise is sometimes looked upon as a contributing factor in high blood pressure, heart conditions, and emotional disturbances.

Basic food requirements may be summarized briefly:

1. Carbohydrates are the main energy fuel sources which compensate for the oxidation and heat-energy losses in metabolism. Requirements depend on activity, averaging about 3,000 calories per day, and balance the daily energy output.
2. Protein is required for the repair maintenance of organic structure and tissue. Though less in volume-demand than carbohydrate, an average of 100 grams per day (or 1.5 grams per kilo of body weight) is estimated as the minimal need.
3. Minerals, vitamins, and a number of trace elements are required for adequate human function. Much attention has been given in recent years to the question of trace elements in human diet; the part played by mineral and other deficiencies in growth, retardation, etc.

Our emphasis in the above sketch of biophysical requirement has been on basic needs. We may also note how such basic needs are subject to psychosocial adjustment. Though we "hunger" biologically, we are generally hungry at socially conditioned intervals, and for a given range of culturally defined foods prepared in quite specific ways.

This sociocultural modification of biophysical function also overlaps, for example, into the technological system as various biophysical modifications, through sophisticated technical means, become relatively routine. Artificial organs and extensions of organs are now operating, as well as electronically controlled limbs and "natural" organ transplants.

The most striking extension through such scientific and technological means has been the general increase in human life expectancy and improved physiological function throughout the life span.

Around 1700, life expectancy at birth of the European populations was about 33 years, and had increased little in the previous three to four hundred years. By 1950, life expectancy in Western and Central Europe and in the United States had increased to 66 to 69 years, an increase of over 100 percent. In 1946, the death rate of the Moslem population of Algeria was higher than that of Sweden in 1775. In 1954, the death rate of this population was lower than that of Sweden in 1875.[32]

These developments in biophysical control are specific aspects of the general advance of knowledge of the function of the human organism in its environ. The interaction of the medical and bioengineering sciences which this entails is also evident in the areas of external metabolism such as water supply, waste disposal systems, food processing and preservation, air purification and conditioning, etc.

We may sense here that the growing ecosystem approach is begining to operate at both the micro and macro extremities of human environ control—within the human body itself, and outwardly to encompass the entire planetary body.

WORLD POPULATION AND FOOD. We tend to think of the food/population problem as peculiar to our own period, but the balance between population growth and food supply has been a constant factor in human development.

Up till our own period, with the industrial revolution and the introduction of mechanized agriculture, most of humanity lived within a narrow margin of feast or famine. The size of human communities was relatively restricted by their close relation to adequate food supply among other factors; e.g., before the mid-1800s few cities got beyond a million inhabitants. By the end of the century, many European cities had multiplied sixfold in two generations.

The beginning capacity to feed more people off the land than on it is directly attributable to successive agri-technological developments.

The paleolithic hunter required 10 square kilometers per person to feed himself. The neolithic herdsmen required 0.1 square kilometers (or 10 hectares). The medieval peasant required two-thirds a hectare of ploughland—to produce cereals for subsistence. The Indian rice grower required one-fifth of a hectare to produce subsistence. The Japanese required one-sixteenth of a hectare or only 640 square meters.[33]

World population quickened when the "feast or famine" cycle was disturbed by improved agricultural practice around the year 1200, and began its present upswing in the 200 years between the sixteenth and eighteenth centuries rising most sharply in the nineteenth century. In the past 150 years, there has been an increase of approximately 2½

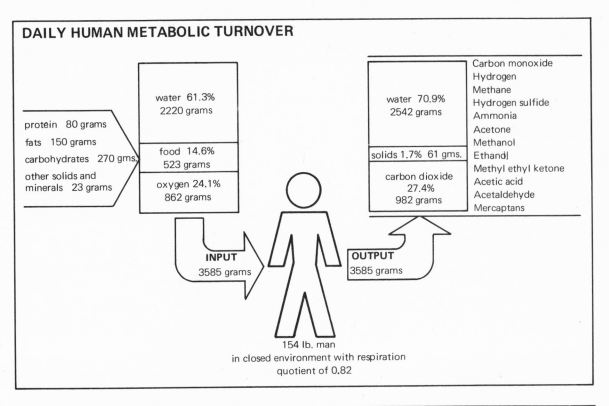

DAILY HUMAN METABOLIC TURNOVER

protein 80 grams
fats 150 grams
carbohydrates 270 gms.
other solids and minerals 23 grams

water 61.3%
2220 grams

food 14.6%
523 grams

oxygen 24.1%
862 grams

water 70.9%
2542 grams

solids 1.7% 61 gms.

carbon dioxide
27.4%
982 grams

Carbon monoxide
Hydrogen
Methane
Hydrogen sulfide
Ammonia
Acetone
Methanol
Ethanol
Methyl ethyl ketone
Acetic acid
Acetaldehyde
Mercaptans

INPUT
3585 grams

OUTPUT
3585 grams

154 lb. man
in closed environment with respiration
quotient of 0.82

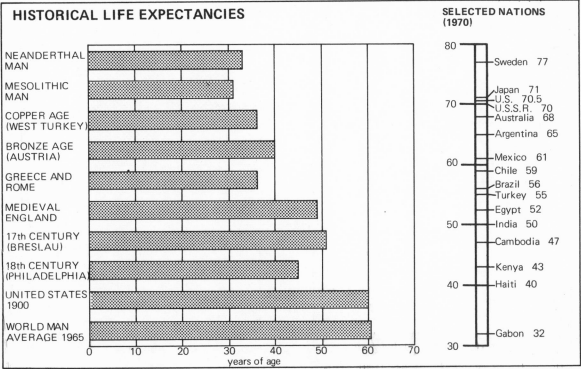

HISTORICAL LIFE EXPECTANCIES

SELECTED NATIONS (1970)

NEANDERTHAL MAN
MESOLITHIC MAN
COPPER AGE (WEST TURKEY)
BRONZE AGE (AUSTRIA)
GREECE AND ROME
MEDIEVAL ENGLAND
17th CENTURY (BRESLAU)
18th CENTURY (PHILADELPHIA)
UNITED STATES 1900
WORLD MAN AVERAGE 1965

0   10   20   30   40   50   60   70
years of age

Sweden 77
Japan 71
U.S. 70.5
U.S.S.R. 70
Australia 68
Argentina 65
Mexico 61
Chile 59
Brazil 56
Turkey 55
Egypt 52
India 50
Cambodia 47
Kenya 43
Haiti 40
Gabon 32

billion in the world population—which had been running at approximately ½ billion for about one thouand years.

Though food supply and population growth may be correlated historically, after a specific stage in human development, this relation is not so directly associated. For example, just when Malthus predicted that the earth's population was increasing beyond the limits of possible food supply—(i.e., that population was increasing geometrically and food supply only arithmetically—we were beginning to triple food yield per acre. Since Malthus' time, we have accommodated more people with more adequate and sustained food supply and higher living standards than in any previous period.

Paradoxically, of course, increased food supply has been accompanied by developments in medical science—giving lower infant mortality, longer life, and better health expectations—all factors contributing to an explosive increase in overall population.

Present world population is just over 3.5 billion. The current rate of increase is about 1.8 percent annually, giving a doubling in 30 to 40 years; i.e., by the year 2000, world population will be over six billion at median estimate. If this growth rate were sustained, there would be over 12 billion on earth in just 70 years.

> . . . The rate of increase in population varies from 1.5 to 3.5 percent per year in most regions. The highest rate of increase occurs in those countries with the lowest per capita food production and income. According to the 1963 FAO Third World Food Survey ". . . should the population grow according to the United Nations 'medium' projection, the world's total food supply would have to be trebled by the year 2000 in order to provide a reasonably adequate level of nutrition. For the less developed areas total food supplies would need to be quadrupled and the supplies of animal products should be raised nine times the present volume." [34]

The developing nations of Asia, for instance, now contain more than half the total number of people in the world . . . and are adding nearly a million more each week! From net grain exporters a generation ago, the developing nations have now become importers of more than 30 million tons of grain a year in their desperate efforts to feed a populace that can no longer be sustained by the primitive tillage of their own soils.[35]

Current cause for alarm about this population explosion is that doubling the number of people in one generation means not only doubling the food supply—but doubling housing needs, doubling and tripling city sizes, highways, agri-industrial extraction, production, transportation, etc., with concomitant doubling and tripling of energy and materials required to maintain living standards.

There is no one simple set of short-range solutions to this problem. We will obviously need to employ as many strategies of population control as are feasible and humanly possible.

For the longer term, however, we may note that population growth is the highest in those world regions which:

1. are technologically underdeveloped.
2. have a high population to usable resource ratio.
3. have a low physical life expectancy.
4. have low social expectations.

On the other hand, growth is lowest (or more stable) in those regions which

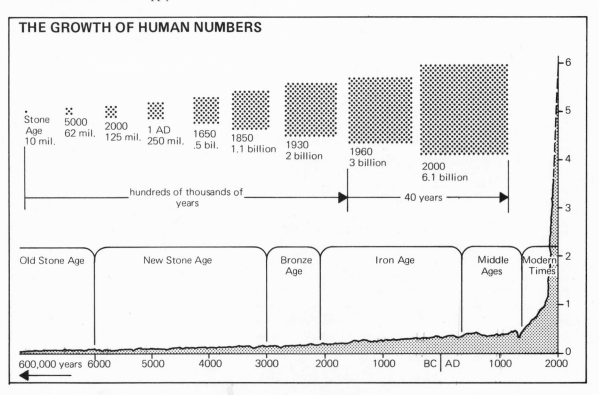

THE GROWTH OF HUMAN NUMBERS

1. are technologically advanced.
2. have a low population to usable resource radio.
3. have a high physical life expectancy.
4. have higher social expectations—that is, in mobility, education, life style, etc.

The evidence suggests that the sharpest decline in birthrate and stable use of birth control, family planning, etc., correlates with sectors receiving the largest share of, and access to, higher living standards and advanced socioeconomic developments. The most effective, and realistic, long-range mode of stabilizing world population would be to raise the living standards and life chance expectations of the lesser developed regions as soon as possible.

The question of feasibility here is, of course, obscured by the older moralities of national competi-

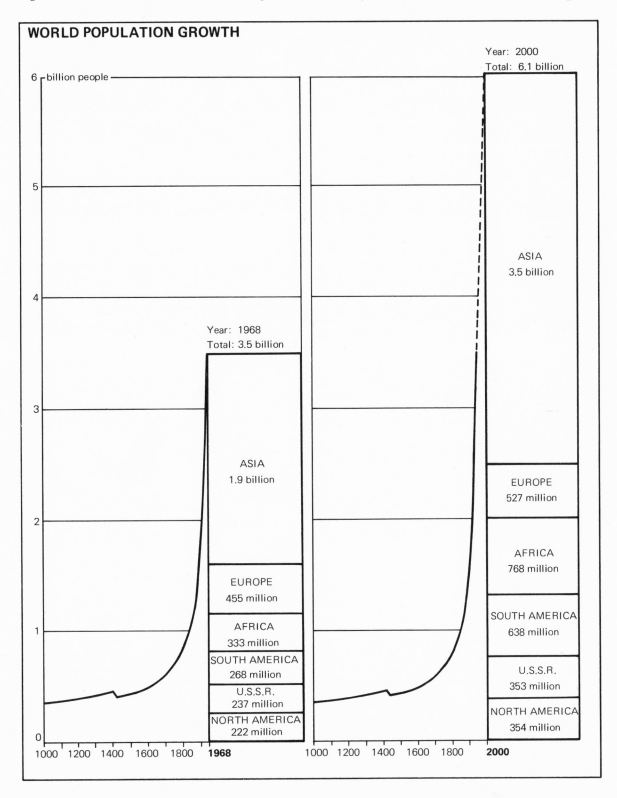

WORLD POPULATION GROWTH

Year: 1968
Total: 3.5 billion

ASIA
1.9 billion

EUROPE
455 million

AFRICA
333 million

SOUTH AMERICA
268 million

U.S.S.R.
237 million

NORTH AMERICA
222 million

1000 1200 1400 1600 1800 **1968**

Year: 2000
Total: 6.1 billion

ASIA
3.5 billion

EUROPE
527 million

AFRICA
768 million

SOUTH AMERICA
638 million

U.S.S.R.
353 million

NORTH AMERICA
354 million

1000 1200 1400 1600 1800 **2000**

MAJOR AREAS OF WORLD POPULATION

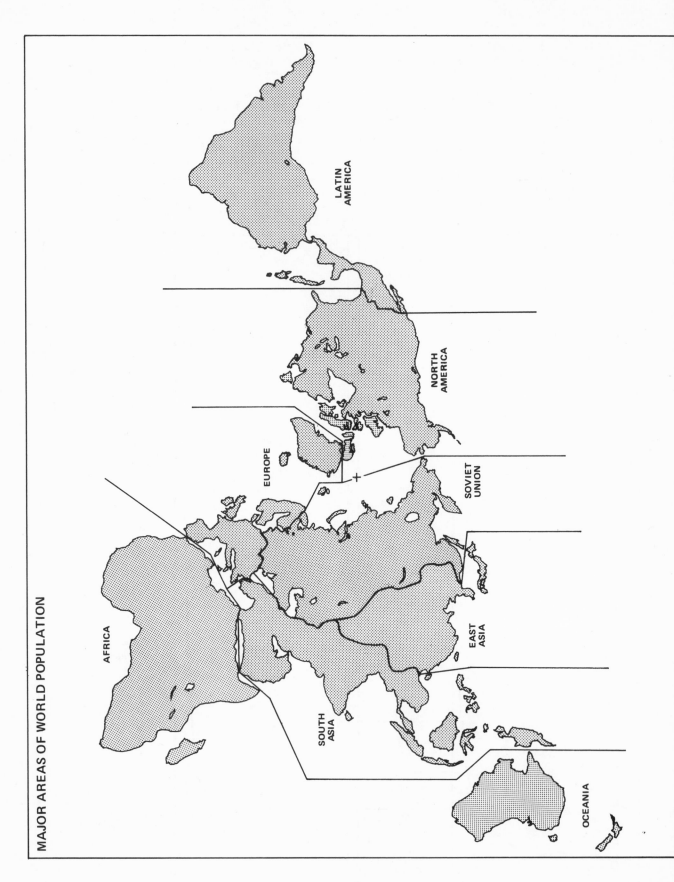

LATIN
AMERICA

NORTH
AMERICA

EUROPE

SOVIET
UNION

AFRICA

EAST
ASIA

SOUTH
ASIA

OCEANIA

WORLD POPULATION

Region / Country	Population Estimates Mid 1970 (Millions)	Current Rate of Population Growth	Number of Years to Double Population	Population Projection to 2000 (Millions)	Per Capita Gross National Product ($)	Population Increase 1965–1970 (Millions)
WORLD	**3632**	**2.0**	**35**	**6795**		**343**
AFRICA	**344**	**2.6**	**27**	**733**		**41**
NORTHERN AFRICA	87	3.1	23	200		12.1
Algeria	14.0	3.2	22	33.7	250	2.2
Libya	1.9	3.1	22	4.4	720	0.3
Morocco	15.7	3.3	21	38.1	190	2.4
Sudan	15.8	3.0	22	37.3	90	2.2
Tunisia	5.1	3.0	22	11.5	210	0.7
UAR	33.9	2.8	25	74.6	160	4.4
WESTERN AFRICA	101	2.6	27	209		11.7
Dahomey	2.7	2.6	27	5.7	80	0.3
Gambia	0.4	1.9	37	0.7	90	0.03
Ghana	9.0	2.9	24	20.2	200	1.3
Guinea	3.9	2.3	30	7.7	90	0.4
Ivory Coast	4.3	2.4	29	8.7	230	0.5
Liberia	1.2	1.9	37	2.1	190	0.1
Mali	5.1	2.1	32	10.4	80	0.6
Mauritania	1.2	2.2	32	2.4	130	0.1
Niger	4.0	2.2	32	8.5	70	0.5
Nigeria	55.1	2.6	27	116.3	80	6.4
Senegal	3.9	2.3	29	7.8	190	0.4
Sierra Leone	2.6	2.4	29	5.1	140	0.3
Togo	1.9	2.6	27	4.0	100	0.2
Upper Volta	5.4	2.6	27	10.3	50	0.5
EASTERN AFRICA	98	2.3	31	207		11.4
Burundi	3.6	2.1	33	7.1	50	0.4
Ethiopia	25.0	2.1	33	47.8	60	2.4
Kenya	10.9	2.9	26	26.4	120	1.5
Madagascar	6.9	2.7	26	14.9	100	0.9
Malawi	4.4	2.5	28	9.1	60	0.5
Mauritius	0.9	2.1	33	1.4	220	0.1
Mozambique	7.7	2.1	33	14.7	180	0.7
Reunion	0.5	3.1	23	1.1	560	0.1
Rwanda	3.6	2.9	24	8.1	50	0.5
Somalia	2.8	2.4	29	5.7	50	0.3
Southern Rhodesia	5.1	3.4	21	12.1	230	1.6
Tanzania	13.2	2.6	27	27.9	80	1.0
Uganda	8.6	2.6	27	18.2	100	0.6
Zambia	4.3	3.0	24	9.7	180	0.6
MIDDLE AFRICA	36	3.0	24	70		3.6
Angola	5.7	2.1	32	10.9	190	0.5
Cameroon (West)	5.8	2.2	32	11.2	130	0.6
Central African Republic	1.5	2.2	32	2.9	120	0.1
Chad	3.7	2.2	32	7.5	70	0.4
Congo (Brazzaville)	0.9	1.3	54	1.8	180	0.1
Congo (Democratic Republic)	17.4	2.2	32	33.7	90	1.8
Equatorial Guinea	0.3	1.3	54	0.4	240	0.02
Gabon	0.5	0.9	78	0.7	410	0.02
SOUTHERN AFRICA	23	2.4	29	47		2.5
Botswana	0.6	2.2	32	1.2	90	0.1
Lesotho	1.0	1.8	39	1.9	60	0.1
South Africa	20.1	2.4	29	40.9	590	2.2
Southwest Africa (Namibia)	0.6	2.0	35	1.1		0.1
Swaziland	0.4	3.0	24	0.9	280	0.1
ASIA	**2056**	**2.3**	**31**	**4105**		**223**
SOUTHWEST ASIA	77	2.9	24	173		10.3
Cyprus	0.6	0.9	78	0.8	780	0.02
Iraq	9.7	3.4	21	23.6	230	1.5
Israel	2.9	2.4	29	5.9	1200	0.3
Jordan	2.3	3.3	21	5.6	250	0.3
Kuwait	0.7	8.3	9	2.0	3490	0.2
Lebanon	2.8	3.0	24	6.3	520	0.4
Saudi Arabia	7.7	2.8	25	16.9	350	1.0
Southern Yemen	1.3	3.3	21	2.9	130	0.2
Syria	6.2	2.7	26	12.2	180	0.9
Turkey	35.6	2.7	26	76.7	290	4.4
Yemen	5.7	2.7	26	12.1	90	0.7
MIDDLE SOUTH ASIA	762	2.6	27	1651		96.9
Afghanistan	17.0	2.5	28	35.2	70	1.9
Bhutan	0.8	2.2	32	1.9	60	0.1
Ceylon	12.6	2.4	29	25.5	160	1.4
India	554.6	2.6	27	1170.8	90	67.9
Iran	28.4	3.0	24	63.9	280	3.8
Nepal	11.2	2.3	32	21.7	70	1.2
Pakistan	136.9	3.3	25	332.5	90	20.6
SOUTHEAST ASIA	287	2.8	25	635		37.6
Burma	27.7	2.3	31	53.9	70	3.0
Cambodia	7.1	3.0	24	16.0	130	1.0
Indonesia	121.2	2.9	24	272.7	100	16.3
Laos	3.0	2.5	28	6.2	90	0.4
Malaysia (East and West)	10.8	2.8	25	24.7	290	1.4
Philipines	38.1	3.4	21	92.5	180	5.8
Singapore	2.1	2.4	29	4.6	600	0.2
Thailand	36.2	3.3	21	87.9	130	5.4
North Vietnam	21.2	2.1	33	40.5	100	2.2
South Vietnam	18.0	2.1	33	34.4	120	1.8
EAST ASIA	930	1.8	39	1645		78.1
China (Mainland)	759.6	1.8	39	1343.9	90	64.6
China (Taiwan)	14.2	2.3	31	27.5	270	1.6
Hong Kong	4.2	2.5	28	8.3	620	0.5
Japan	103.5	1.1	63	152.8	1000	5.5
Korea (North)	13.9	2.8	25	30.6	230	1.8
Korea (South)	32.1	2.5	28	66.4	160	3.7
Mongolia	1.3	3.1	23	2.8	410	0.2
NORTH AMERICA	**228**	**1.1**	**63**	**333**		**11.4**
Canada	21.4	1.7	41	37.0	2380	1.4
United States	205.2	1.0	70	292.4	3670	10.5
LATIN AMERICA	**283**	**2.9**	**24**	**625**		**37**
MIDDLE AMERICA	67	3.4	21	163		10.5
Costa Rica	1.8	3.8	19	4.6	410	0.3
El Salvador	3.4	3.4	21	8.3	270	0.5
Guatemala	5.1	2.9	24	11.3	310	0.7
Honduras	2.7	3.4	21	6.6	240	0.4
Mexico	50.7	3.4	21	123.1	490	8.0
Nicaragua	2.0	3.0	24	4.5	360	0.3
Panama	1.5	3.3	21	3.6	550	0.2
CARIBBEAN	26	2.2	32	50		2.7
Barbados	0.3	0.8	88	0.4	420	0.01
Cuba	8.4	1.9	37	15.2	330	0.8
Dominican Republic	4.3	3.4	21	10.4	260	0.7
Guadeloupe	0.4	2.4	29	0.8	470	0.04
Haiti	5.2	2.5	28	10.8	70	0.6
Jamaica	2.0	2.1	33	3.8	460	0.2
Martinique	0.4	2.0	35	0.7	540	0.03
Puerto Rico	2.8	1.4	50	4.5	1210	0.2
Trinidad and Tobago	1.1	1.8	39	1.9	790	0.1
TROPICAL SOUTH AMERICA	151	3.0	24	340		20.8
Bolivia	4.6	2.8	25	9.0	170	0.5
Brazil	93.0	2.8	25	204.6	250	12.3
Colombia	21.4	3.4	21	51.9	300	3.3
Ecuador	6.1	2.9	24	14.9	210	1.0
Guyana	0.7	3.1	23	1.6	330	0.1
Peru	13.6	3.1	23	31.3	350	1.9
Venezuela	10.8	3.4	21	26.2	880	1.6
TEMPERATE SOUTH AMERICA	39	1.8	39	70		3.4
Argentina	24.3	1.5	47	39.8	800	1.7
Chile	9.8	2.3	31	19.3	470	1.1
Paraguay	2.4	3.4	21	5.8	220	0.4
Uruguay	2.9	1.2	58	4.4	550	0.2
EUROPE	**462**	**0.8**	**88**	**620**		**18**
NORTHERN EUROPE	81	0.6	117	102		2.3
Denmark	4.9	0.8	88	5.5	1950	0.1
Finland	4.7	0.4	175	5.5	1660	0.1
Iceland	0.2	1.8	39	0.3	1690	0.02
Ireland	3.0	0.7	100	3.7	910	0.1
Norway	3.9	0.9	78	4.7	1860	0.2
Sweden	8.0	0.8	88	10.7	2500	0.3
United Kingdom	56.0	0.5	140	68.0	1700	1.4
WESTERN EUROPE	149	0.8	88	200		5.5
Austria	7.4	0.4	175	8.6	1210	0.4
Belgium	9.7	0.4	175	11.4	1740	0.4
France	51.1	0.8	88	68.5	1950	2.4
West Germany	58.6	0.6	117	73.6	1750	2.7
Luxembourg	0.4	1.2	58	0.6	2150	0.02
Netherlands	13.0	1.1	63	19.2	1520	0.7
Switzerland	6.3	1.1	63	9.3	2310	0.3
EASTERN EUROPE	104	0.8	88	139		4.0
Bulgaria	8.5	0.8	88	11.4	690	0.3
Czechoslovakia	14.7	0.7	100	18.3	1110	0.5
East Germany	16.2	0.3	233	12.0	1300	0.2
Hungary	10.3	0.4	175	12.9	900	0.5
Poland	33.0	1.3	54	45.8	780	1.5
Romania	20.3	1.0	70	31.6	720	1.3
SOUTHERN EUROPE	128	0.9	78	177		5.7
Albania	2.2	2.7	26	4.7	320	0.3
Greece	8.9	0.8	88	11.9	700	0.3
Italy	53.7	0.8	88	72.0	1120	0.8
Malta	0.3	0.7	100	0.2	570	−0.01
Portugal	9.6	−0.7		12.5	420	0.2
Spain	33.2	1.1	63	47.4	680	1.6
Yugoslavia	20.6	1.1	70	27.3	530	1.6
U.S.S.R.	242.6	1.0	70	347	970	12.1
OCEANIA	**19**	**2.0**	**35**	**35**		**2.0**
Australia	12.5	1.9	37	22.6	1970	1.0
New Zealand	2.9	1.7	41	5.0	1890	0.2

tion, local insecurities, and lack of understanding of the changes in world society itself. Whether such advances could come quickly enough to avert the presently unfavorable balance is questionable. Simple questions such as, "Could we afford it in world terms?" may be as simply answered: the ten percent of the world's gross product presently preoccupied in military and associated defense expenditures could affect dramatic changes if reallocated to our real "security" imperatives!

The world food problem has somewhat the same profile of imbalance, inadequacy, and urgent need for the reallocation of national and world priorities.

> At present U.S. levels of technology, and taking into account the cultivated area necessary for non-food crops, it would be possible to produce 4,500 calories per person per day for foodstuffs and live-stock feed for five billion people. This is only 20 percent more than the population expected by the end of this century. At present levels of productivity per acre, the potential gross cropped area would provide no more than a bare subsistence diet for the population expected by about 1990. The needed increase of food supplies, because it involves overall economic development will involve very large capital investments, probably a transfer of five to ten billion dollars more per year from the rich countries to the poor ones than is now the case, as well as a very high level of technical assistance in research, experimentation, education, and expert advice.[36]

Though the Western one-third of the world's population generally speaks in terms of basic nutritional adequacy, we consume roughly five times the basic food requirements that we suggest as minimal for the hungry nations.

Of the other two-thirds of the world population, the greater majority live on a marginal basis—either close to physical starvation or closely dependent on the vagaries of local climatic and crop variation to keep above the famine line.

It is important also to underline here that of the doubling of world population, which is admitted as a major world survival problem, over 80 percent of that increase will be in those world regions which are now below adequate nutritional standards for full growth and development (Asia, Africa, and Latin America).

As the main link in the poverty chain of malnutrition, infectious disease, infestation, and low productivity, food would appear to have priority. Man cannot live effectively when chronically hungry. He cannot work or study efficiently, nor reason well beyond his next meal. His resistance to disease is lowered and his whole potential as a human being is at a low ebb. Not only does early malnutrition stunt physical growth, but it has now been shown to retard mental growth. The chronically hungry are thus in a double bind—with insufficient physical energies and a possible decline in mental energy resources to cope with these problems locally.

During the World Food Congress, June, 1963, it was stated:

> Every day of this week some 10,000 will die of malnutrition or starvation. In India alone, 50 million children will die of malnutrition in the next ten years. More than half of the world's three billion people live in perpetual hunger.

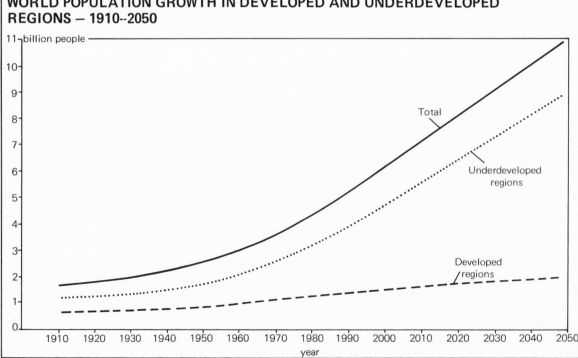

WORLD POPULATION GROWTH IN DEVELOPED AND UNDERDEVELOPED REGIONS — 1910--2050

This picture has not altered greatly in the past seven years.

The comparative per capita daily consumption, still conceals deficiencies. For example, the average person in a high standard country consumes approximately four pounds of food per day as against about 1¼ pounds of food per person in the low standard areas; but, the former is higher not only in weight but in dietary value. The necessary protein for growth and health requires inclusion in the diet of meat, fowl, fish, eggs, milk, cheese products, etc. The high standard diet contains more than 20 percent of such products; the low standard, less than 5 percent. In some countries it may be 85 percent rice, deficient in protein, fats, and vitamins.

Cereal grains occupy more than 70 percent of the world's crop lands. Consumed directly, they provide more than half of our total food energy and indirectly, via animal foods, take care of the remainder. This is the preferred adequate balance. In the poorer regions, however, the direct consumption of grains provides almost three-quarters of the available food.

So behind the mere provision of adequate amounts of food lies the difference in balance; e.g., the North American diet includes 25 percent of livestock products, the European diet includes 17 percent of livestock products and the Asian includes only 3 percent of livestock products. The latter, thereby, has the further inadequacies and deficiencies noted above.

With this reliance on a bulk diet of cereal grains in the poorer world regions, if production of grains does not rise in any one year, there is then not only the population increase of 60 or 70 million extra people to feed in these regions, but the increased numbers who slip over into outright starvation.

GROSS FOOD NEEDS AND REQUIREMENTS
1975-2000

	Increase in total food supply needed to MAINTAIN present diet levels	Increase in food supply needed to IMPROVE present diet levels	
		total supply	animal foods
1975	35%	50%	60%
1985	50%	85%	130%
2000	75%	124%	210%

REQUIRED PRODUCTION INCREASES
1975-2000

product	increases necessary	
	1975	2000
Cereals	35%	110%
Pulses and nuts	85%	225%
Animal products	60%	210% [37]

THE GREEN REVOLUTION

For most . . . the outstanding technological achievement of this generation was the landing on the moon . . . but for one billion Asians for whom rice is the staple food, the development of IR-8 and its dissemination throughout Asia is a more mean-

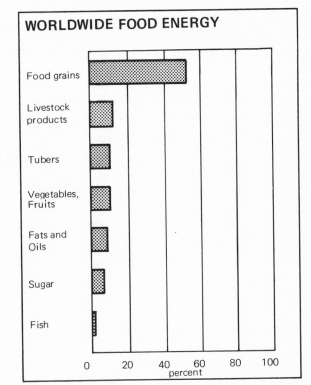

WORLDWIDE FOOD ENERGY

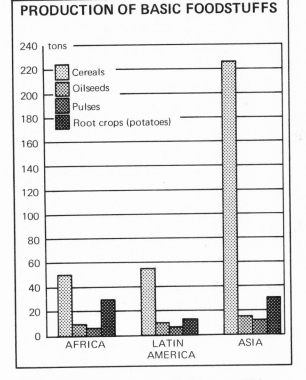

PRODUCTION OF BASIC FOODSTUFFS

ingful achievement. It is literally helping to fill hundreds of millions of rice bowls once only half full. For those for whom hunger is a way of life, technology can offer no greater reward.[38]

As stressed before, the new miracle high-yield grains now constitute "a green revolution" in the poorer world regions in direct and local gain in food production, but dramatic as this is, it can only at best give us a slender time margin to deal further with the world food problem. The real message of the green revolution lies with its multiplier effect, the amount of change, in a seemingly insoluble world problem, which was effected with a relatively minuscule amount of funds plus the dedicated energies of a small proportion of the world's scientists.

It is, of course, not only the scientists and technologists who are responsible for the vast and rapid acceptance of the new seeds but the millions of farmers, particularly in Asia, who decided to plant them and in so doing found their incomes increasing two-, three-, and even fourfold. The area planted to high-yielding cereals in Asia in the 1964-65 crop year was estimated at 200 acres, and that largely for experimental and trial purposes. By 1968-69, 34 million acres were covered. . . . Because they proved so profitable to farmers, adoption of the new varieties spread far more rapidly than was anticipated, raising cereal production at an unexpected rate. If it is assumed that replacement of local varieties with high-yielding seeds raised output by a half-ton per acre—a conservative assumption—the 34 million acres planted in 1968-69 expanded the Asian food supply by 17 million tons, roughly the equivalent of two billion dollars worth of grain! [39]

1964-65	200	total acres in production
1965-66	37,000	,, ,, ,, ,,
1966-67	4,800,000	,, ,, ,, ,,
1967-68	20,000,000	,, ,, ,, ,,
1968-69	34,000,000	,, ,, ,, ,,
1969-70	40,000,000	,, ,, ,, ,, 40

The approaches toward the solution of the world food problem are not all direct; i.e., instead of just increasing food production, they require less obvious

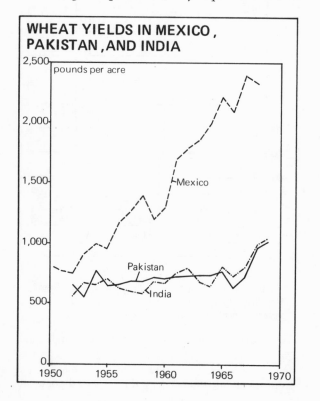

WHEAT YIELDS IN MEXICO, PAKISTAN, AND INDIA

but more important aspects of world social and economic reorganization. Though we often focus on the amount of food given by the richer to the poorer in direct aid, less attention is given to the much greater amounts of indirect annual foodstuffs—soybeans, oilseed cake, fishmeal—imported by the richer nations from the poorer. Many of the latter are forced to export food and other resources for manufactured goods and materials they do not produce, but which have been produced in many cases from their exported resources. Millions of food producers in the poor, tropical regions are still forced to raise cash crops of cotton, bananas, coffee, tea, cocoa, etc., to exchange indirectly for food protein they might otherwise produce themselves.

Eventually, we must break the local land dependence ties. No country has progressed toward adequate nutrition for its population and avoidance of recurring famine until at least half of its population has moved from agriculture to industry. In the industrial countries, less than ten percent of the labor force produces more than enough food for the whole population.

In 1945, one farm worker fed and clothed 14.6 people in the United States. Today he feeds and clothes three times as many.[41]
In the past 20 years, crop production per acre and livestock production per breeding unit have increased almost 40 percent . . . accomplished with a labor force that diminished almost 40 percent. . . . Our markets for dairy products are now supplied by some 10 million fewer cows than were needed 20 years ago.[42]

As with the population crisis, apart from immediate stop gap measures, the only viable and realistic solutions in the longer term may be sought via multiple approaches—involving massive reordering of world priorities and with equivalent inputs of funds, energies and expertise on a par with our military and space programs.

WORLD HEALTH. Health and life expectancy are among the most markedly unbalanced factors in the relations between the "have" and "have not" areas of the world.

Health cannot be taken for granted when about 75 percent of the world's inhabitants are without an adequate and safe supply of water, when 85 percent depend on the most primitive methods for the disposal of excreta and refuse.[43]
Underscoring the inadequacy of community facilities, the report cited the findings of the World Health Organization that one hospital bed out of four is occupied by a patient who is ill because of polluted water.
The report said: "In 75 developing countries only 33 percent of townsfolk have running water indoors or in the yard, another third have easy access to public outlets and the remainder have to be content with what they find." [44]

In the lesser developed regions of the world, close to 380 million are still exposed to malaria, ten

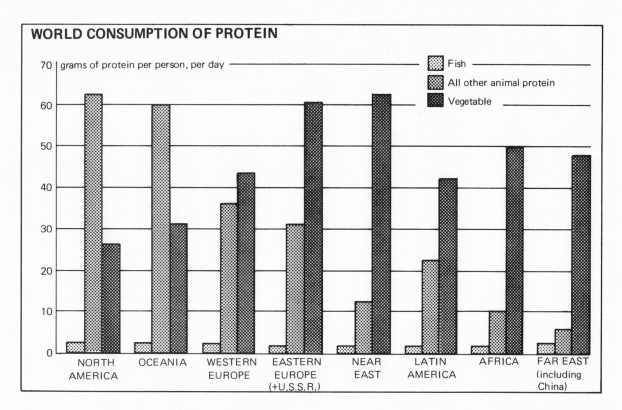

WORLD CONSUMPTION OF PROTEIN

70 | grams of protein per person, per day

Fish
All other animal protein
Vegetable

NORTH AMERICA · OCEANIA · WESTERN EUROPE · EASTERN EUROPE (+U.S.S.R.) · NEAR EAST · LATIN AMERICA · AFRICA · FAR EAST (including China)

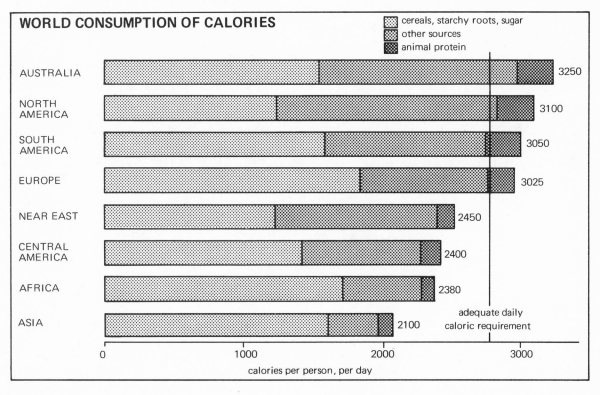

WORLD CONSUMPTION OF CALORIES

cereals, starchy roots, sugar
other sources
animal protein

	calories per person, per day
AUSTRALIA	3250
NORTH AMERICA	3100
SOUTH AMERICA	3050
EUROPE	3025
NEAR EAST	2450
CENTRAL AMERICA	2400
AFRICA	2380
ASIA	2100

adequate daily caloric requirement

calories per person, per day

million suffer from leprosy, and more than 4½ million are ravaged by yaws. Schistosomiasis, a chronic infection caused by a blood parasite, today threatens some 200 million people and has not been wholly checked. Approximately one-third of the world's population suffers from ill health in one form or another; in many areas half the children die before the age of five, largely as a result of malnutrition.

Every half minute, 100 children are born in developing countries. Twenty of them will die within the year. Of the 80 who survive, 60 will have no access to modern medical care during their childhood.

An equal number will suffer from malnutrition during the crucial weaning and toddler age—with the possibility of irreversible physical and mental damage; and during this period their chance of dying will be 20 to 40 times higher than if they lived in Europe or North America . . . in some developing states 30 to 40 percent of the children die before reaching the age of 5.[45]

. . . the wealthy nations of the world ignore the health problems of the less developed nations at their peril. Modern transportation systems make possible the global spread of infectious disease with great speed. Pockets of disease and disease vectors serve as natural time bombs, threatening danger at any time. Drugs and sera—their development, production, and availability in time of need—are of concern to all nations. Organizations for the detection of disease and medical problems cannot be other than international. Similarly, the world as a global unit is concerned with the total availability and services, and with the standards of health and medical care. [46]

Those living in the developed regions have seen the past pattern of disease change within their own lifetime and life expectancy rise by almost twenty years. The greater proportion of this gain is not wholly due to curative medicine but to the enlarged role of preventive medicine and its extension toward envionmental medicine—and this gain has cost relatively little compared to other material advances. Diseases which were formerly great killers—cholera, typhoid, dysentery—have almost disappeared not only because of direct medical intervention and new drugs, but through regulation of the water supply. Environmental sanitation has reduced malaria, yellow fever, and tuberculosis. Preventive vaccinations have nearly eliminated smallpox, diphtheria, and polio.

The health problems of the "high standard" nations now reflect, in part, their population make-up,

with degenerative diseases high, as in the aged; and, in other ways, their present lack of "ecological design" in the use of the industrial complex. Many of the respiratory diseases, allergies, and cancers, whose causal agencies are not completely determined, may be linked to chemical pollutants in the atmosphere; overloaded sewage and water control systems still pollute rivers, lakes, and streams with accompanying disease.

> Over two million Americans are stricken with illness each year from microbiological contamination of food, causing an estimated annual loss of 1.5 million work days. Salmonella contamination of food accounts for at least 50 percent of the work days lost.[47]

Another aspect is the reported increase in the proportion of mental illness. This has been estimated as accounting for almost 50 percent of all hospital accommodations in England and the United States. A considerable number of such patients, e.g., 21 percent in England, are over sixty-five years of age. This apparent increase would tend to be explicable by an increase in recognition, concern, and care for the mentally ill, and by the proportion of older persons whose lack of adaptation to rapid change has engendered various stress conditions.

PSYCHOSOCIAL

Man is human by virtue of his social existence: "social patterns determine biological events." He lives in, by, and for human society. Society, in this case, is not confined to local society, but to the

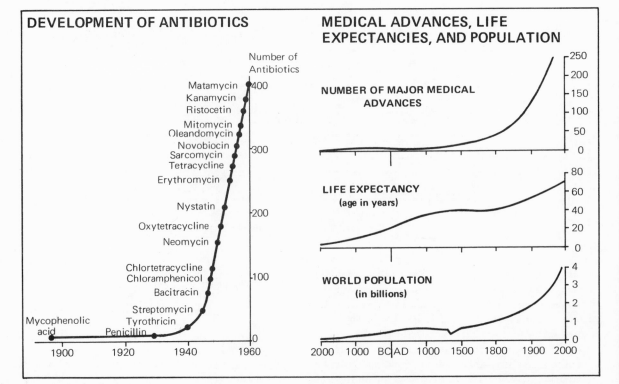

awareness of, and sense of belonging to, the larger human society: to the continuity of human cultural experience. Meaning, even for the individual, cannot be separated from its location within this social context.

Man is made human by his earliest experiences of human contact. He learns to be a human being. When acutely deprived of such early periods of socialization, the organism exists, but is so limited in mental and even physical development that basic survival itself is impaired.

Thought we may stress an "ecological" approach, this remains almost exclusively man focused, a bias we cannot escape. We perceive the environment only in human-related terms. No matter how "objective" we may strive to be, the formulation of objectivity is itself a peculiarly human symbolic process.

> . . . the qualities and characteristics that constitute the visual sensations of which we are conscious . . . are not inherent in the so-called external "things" at which we are looking. The origin of our sensations is in the prior experiences and the characteristics and qualities of our sensations are determined by our unique personal (social) history, etc.[48]

The prime vehicle for all our environmental interpretation and the basis for human action is some form of language. Both verbal and non-verbal symbolic languages "order" our perception of the environ and control the interpretation and communication of what we perceive. Language constructs our reality.

It is suggested that man stopped "physically" evolving about 150,000 years ago and now tends to offload his evolution socially through various extensions. Much of his apparently irrational behavior is explicable as "instinctual" responses which were biologically meaningful, but which are no longer appropriate to his changed condition. Fears and insecurities expressed in certain "dominance, territoriality, crowd, and flight responses," which had great survival value in past states, may often act to negative advantage in the present unless positively channeled and/or symbolically transformed when they may become sources of social energy.

Man's ecological expansion has been particularly characterized by the way in which accumulated knowledge about the environ is preserved and passed on through succeeding generations. This forms part of the major evolutionary step in the adaptability of the organism. This function of transmitting social and cultural experience and of regulating social interaction through symbolic extensions has led to the complex growth of human institutions, of human society. His evolution is more directly that of a psychosocial and increasingly conscious development.

As man in isolation, and in small community groups, could only develop conceptual and physical control of his environ to a particular level, so also his successive interlinkage in larger units, e.g., from tribe to city to city-state and nation, has been accompanied by his progressive conceptual enlargement and control of more complex systems.

This hypothesis of physical and conceptual enlargement toward an optimal population and "ideomass" as prerequisites for various levels of human developmental control has been particularly explored recently:

> Man fully emerged as the cultural Homo sapiens some 40 thousand years ago when he perfected his ability to elaborate conceptual space. Since then, each doubling of conceptual space has permitted an accompanying doubling of population in a very orderly manner. So effective became the ability to develop conceptual space that each successive doubling of population required only half the time as for the prior doubling. Imbedded in this process of accelerating human progression lies the striving for, and realization of ever enlarging networks of communication and interdependence. From bands to clans, to tribes, to nations, to empires) to leagues, in ascending magnitude of mutual identity, support, and sovereignity the web enlarges. Completion of this historic process, this first era of human evolution, will see the web of all humanity finally become a single accepted network before another century passes.[49]

One may develop this further: the mastery of complexity and degree of conscious control of human affairs now necessary at the global level could not have been reached at any of the previously localized and dispersed stages of human existence. In order for the system to become consciously self-steering, it had to attain to an "optimal critical mass" of globally interacting individuals, ideas, and organizations.

> . . . the human race (now) represents a self-steering system composed of 3.6 billion personalities in different phases of biological and cultural evolution. As in similar cybernetic systems, homeostasis of a biological system such as the human race is conditioned by a quality and quantity of information uniting a self-steering mechanism.[50]

Social evolution in this sense may be likened to a cybernetic process, one that is oriented to its goals by "feedback." Increased, and more highly organized, information about the environ and the society as an integral ongoing process is fed back in due proportion so as to "guide" future development.

The bio-evolutionary direction appears to be set toward increased complexity of psychosocial order as human information increases, accumulates, and is refined into conceptual means for operating on the overall environ.

Man's function in the ecosystem may then be viewed as:

1. Entropic: where man uses energies to reduce complex material resources to simpler structures, that is, where he acts as an "unconscious" biological agent as in food processing, reducing, and ex-

tinguishing other organic populations, disordering toward malfunction of "natural" systems, in air, water, earth pollution, and so forth.

2. Anti-entropic: where he uses energies more consciously to modify and transform his environ toward higher levels of complexity. Through the application of organized information/knowledge in his artificial systems, he increasingly reprocesses, reorders, and redistributes energy and materials in more, rather than less, complex forms.

The balance between his entropic (disordering) propensities and his anti-entropic (ordering) propensities is, in this sense, a central point of our present discussions. We can only surmise, in terms of our brief historical record, that this balance is already tipped, through evolutionary development, toward the anti-entropic as more favorable to the survival of the species.

All human action is social action, as all human behavior occurs within some system of socially interactive relationships; that is, even where the specific interaction is with a physical resource or technological artifact, its form and purpose is socially determined.

Though we refer to advanced or modern societies in contrast to the lesser developed, we need to qualify this considerably in psychosocial developmental terms. Human institutional forms and socioeconomic systems change more slowly than technologies and their associated systems.

The most advanced societies may be still viewed as undergoing a painful "three-generation" transition into modern societies. The problems with which they are dealing are still those of craft-oriented, agricultural societies in the first phase of emergence from their nineteenth century origins, whose human systems and internal institutional arrangements are no longer adequate to the twentieth century context and are certainly constraining upon their possible future development.

In general, a great many of the so-called advanced societies are faced with severe dislocation, deterioration, and obsolescence in critical areas of their socioeconomic and political structures. Many of their internal institutions are archaic, strained toward breakdown and confined by nineteenth and early twentieth century concepts and practices. Their physical environments are still suffering from the backlash of their initial developmental phases of unrestrained industrial exploitation.

As the term is used here, modernization implies the conscious redirection and institutional reorganization of preindustrial and craft-industrial societies toward postindustrial forms. Though we refer glibly to the Western scientific and technological societies, no one of these has yet approached the beginnings of what might be termed a "scientific" society, i.e., one whose motivations, goals, and orientations are congruent and permeated with the scientific outlook in the larger sense.

In many cases both the conceptual and working models of these societies and their stated goals and objectives are no longer congruent with the internal changes which have already occurred, let alone those which are ongoing or might be anticipated.

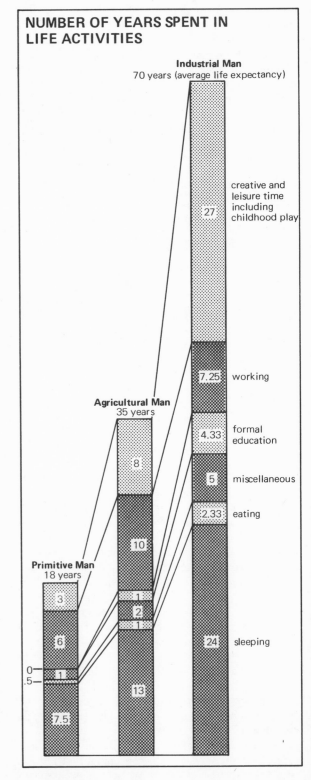

NUMBER OF YEARS SPENT IN LIFE ACTIVITIES

Industrial Man
70 years (average life expectancy)

27 — creative and leisure time including childhood play

7.25 — working

4.33 — formal education

5 — miscellaneous

2.33 — eating

24 — sleeping

Agricultural Man
35 years

8

10

1

2

1

13

Primitive Man
18 years

3

6

0
.5 —

1

7.5

All of our most advanced large-scale industrial enterprises are now service-oriented rather than product manufacturing or marketing institutions. This trend has been further accelerated by the introduction of automated production.

Products may now be manufactured in astronomical quantity runs, with less and less input of human and machine energies. The role of major public or private "business" utilities is, therefore, not so directly concerned with the creation of wealth through material products manufactured, but with the organization and regulation of the wealth of distribution.

There is, then, the shift in emphasis from produc-

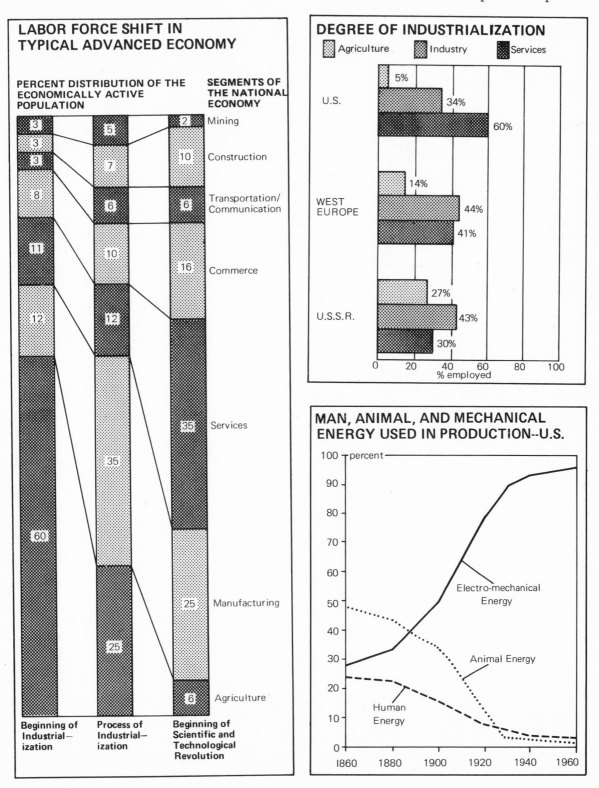

LABOR FORCE SHIFT IN TYPICAL ADVANCED ECONOMY

PERCENT DISTRIBUTION OF THE ECONOMICALLY ACTIVE POPULATION

SEGMENTS OF THE NATIONAL ECONOMY

Mining
Construction
Transportation/Communication
Commerce
Services
Manufacturing
Agriculture

Beginning of Industrialization
Process of Industrialization
Beginning of Scientific and Technological Revolution

DEGREE OF INDUSTRIALIZATION

Agriculture   Industry   Services

U.S.
5%
34%
60%

WEST EUROPE
14%
44%
41%

U.S.S.R.
27%
43%
30%

% employed

MAN, ANIMAL, AND MECHANICAL ENERGY USED IN PRODUCTION--U.S.

percent

Electro-mechanical Energy
Animal Energy
Human Energy

1860 1880 1900 1920 1940 1960

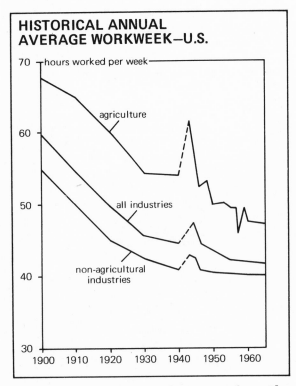

HISTORICAL ANNUAL AVERAGE WORKWEEK—U.S.

hours worked per week

agriculture

all industries

non-agricultural industries

tion and product-sales marketing to the wider concept of the service industry, whether this is in service of supplied products (auto) or service in the full rentable (telephone) facility service.

These developments are paced by changes in occupation and shifts in society's orientation to work, production, leisure, etc. The manual production work declines, as more mechanical energies are poured into production. Supervisory functions vanish as the machine regulates its own work. Inventories no longer need small armies of clerical workers and so on, up through the hierarchy of functions, to include executive control of marketing and distribution functions. There is a corresponding shift of manpower to the service industry vector, but this again may only be viewed as a temporary phenomenon when automated facilities begin to take over large areas of such servicing.

Today human labor provides energy for far less than 1 percent of the work performed in factories, refineries, and mills in the production of their products. Literally, our economy and our way of life could not continue without the use of vast amounts of energy.

One measure of this situation is the increase in the total power for all engines, turbines, and work animals over the past 3 decades. [There has been an] increase from 2.7 billion horsepower available in the United States in 1940 to 17.9 billion in 1968. Of this, engines in trucks, buses, and automobiles accounted for by far the largest part, increasing from 2.5 billion horsepower in 1940 to 16.9 billion horsepower in 1968. Over the same period, the power of electric generating stations increased from 53 million horsepower to 371 million horsepower.[51]

. . . as the productivity in a society increased and the national income began to rise, the bulk of the labor force would begin to shift out of what he called the primary sector. The primary sector is larger agricultural and mining, engaging seventy percent or more of the labor force in unskilled work (a fact still true of the bulk of the countries in the world today). When countries begin to industrialize, the bulk of the labor force shifts into industry, or the secondary sector. But as a country enters into a phase of high consumption, the labor force begins to shift into tertiary (services), quaternary (trade and finance) and quinary (research, recreation, and teaching) sectors. In the past, thus, the increase in white-collar employment has come from the expansion of jobs in government, insurance, banks, schools, and colleges, and the like." [52]

All of this points to the intensive expansion of the service industries concept. Not only to service in lieu of any machine capacity to carry out the task, or service in support of machine supplied items, but toward a vast ecological change in man's whole societal relation. The most phenomenal growth industry is in knowledge processing, both in the expanded capacities to amass, analyze, and use information through the computer and its ancillary "couplings" and expansion in many forms, and in the primary sector of knowledge discovery, communication and development. Education, in the largest sense—as the ordering, discrimination, and discovery of knowledge—is the key growth industry.

We may now produce in abundance many of our material requirements without the need to exact human labor in equable return. In effect, as science and technology are directly based on the availability of all recorded human knowledge, all human equity is already invested in the whole process. The invention of the zero is as relatively important as that of the transistor. It is, therefore, a realistic, rather than merely philosophical, premise that the only universal credit card for access to the fruits of the whole enterprise is membership in the human race!

Human "employment" now comes before and after the facts of "manufacture"—primarily, as an initiation of technological invention, discovery, research, and development; secondly, as "consumer."

The employment curve in reality is an independent line from the point of development of automatic controls. Our present method of "pay for work," through which we distribute wealth, represents a fraction of such reinvestment capacity.

The new wealth generated by industrial technologies is no longer dependent on the old forms of land, materials, and property.

Physical materials are now increasingly interconvertible. They are not used up but are increasingly recycled and reissued in the industrial process. With decreasing input of human and machine energies, physical products have no intrinsic wealth value in themselves other than their human-use value. Material property is no longer a major source of economic power and ownership or a necessary use-relation between people and material goods and services.

RELATIONSHIP OF MAN TO ELECTROMAGNETIC SPECTRUM

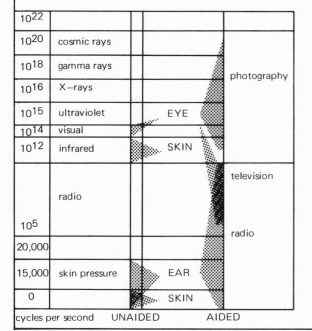

cycles per second			
10^{22}			
10^{20}	cosmic rays		
10^{18}	gamma rays		photography
10^{16}	X—rays		
10^{15}	ultraviolet	EYE	
10^{14}	visual		
10^{12}	infrared	SKIN	
	radio		television
10^{5}			radio
20,000			
15,000	skin pressure	EAR	
0		SKIN	

cycles per second   UNAIDED   AIDED

Sensory Extension. The most abrupt and fundamentally important of the transitions which lead up to our present world developed in the sciences in the late 19th century and became first evident in the technology of World War I. Experimental science began to extend its measurable range into the invisible subsensorial world of atomic, molecular, and "radiation" phenomena.

TOTAL BOOKS PUBLISHED

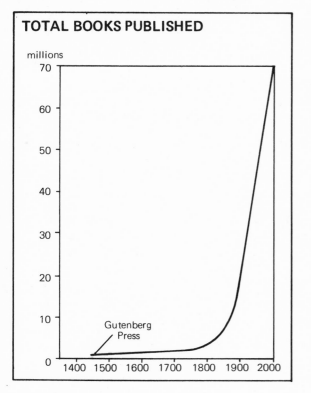

millions

70, 60, 50, 40, 30, 20, 10, 0

1400 1500 1600 1700 1800 1900 2000

Gutenberg Press

SOURCES OF THE WORLD'S CHEMICAL LITERATURE -- 1966	%	LANGUAGES OF THE WORLD'S CHEMICAL LITERATURE	%
U.S.	30.0	English	54.9
U.S.S.R.	21.3	Russian	21.0
Commonwealth	12.2	German	7.1
Germany	6.8	French	5.2
Japan	6.4	Japanese	3.1
France	5.0	Italian	2.1
Czechoslovakia	2.6	Polish	1.8
Poland	2.5	Others	4.8
Italy	2.4		
Others	10.8		
TOTAL	100.0	TOTAL	100.0

INCREASE OF KNOWLEDGE—
THE ELECTROMAGNETIC SPECTRUM

The visual pattern recognition capacity of the eye lens and correlated brain function has been progressively extended and amplified through the simple magnifying lens to the microscope and telescope, through the camera lucida and obscura to the photographic and television camera, and toward sophisticated systems which record, amplify, and relate complex visual and aural patterns of great magnitude.

This development also encompasses the ways in which man has widened his "sensorial" monitoring of the electromagnetic spectrum through instrumentation. He can now "see" into the infra-red, ultra-violet, and X-ray frequencies, "hear" in the radio frequencies, and, may more delicately "feel" through electronic metering than with his most sensitive skin area.

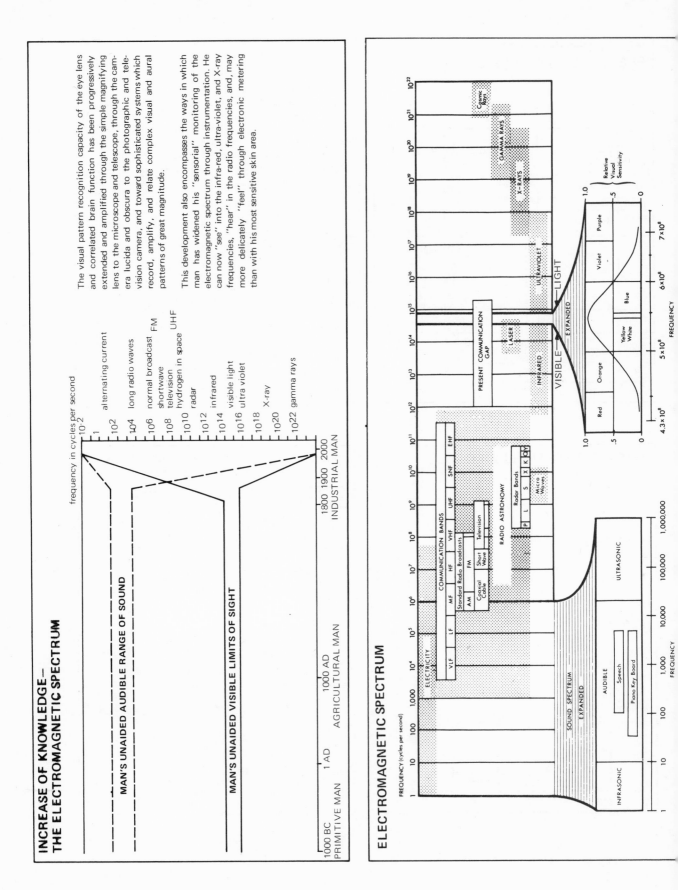

ELECTROMAGNETIC SPECTRUM

Within the new socioeconomic realities of this emergent system, the older conceptual models of scarcity and competitive marginal survival are not only obsolete, but counterproductive and inimical to society's forward development. The new wealth generators, information, knowledge, and organization do not lose in value by any range of distributive sharing—as did the older wealth forms of material resource, land, property—they can only gain.

THE TRANSNATIONAL SOCIETY.   The trends which now lead us collectively into one planetary community are not the old bonds between nations, but forces which operate across national frontiers and with lessening constraint by local territorial sovereignties.

Where previously human society was contained in a discrete number of enclaves spread around inside the biosphere, we now need to conceptualize the other spheres of human activity which surround the planet.

1. The noosphere, as de Chardin has called the film of organized intelligence around the earth, now links myriad individuals in cooperative knowledge enterprises.
2. The sociospheres, econospheres, and technospheres—all the complex and interrelated networks of institutions, organizations, and interdependent technological systems—form a remarkably unified network of human service systems around the planet.

World communications provide commonly shared cultural experiences in a manner unparalleled in human history. Within this network, movies, television, radio, magazines, and newspapers are a common cultural environ sharing and transmitting man's symbolic needs and expressions on a world scale. We may note here how swiftly all major contemporary movements and events move around the world by viewing, for example, the movement of youth life styles: London today, Tokyo tomorrow, Mexico City and Peking the day after. Changes in clothes, music, cosmetics, and chemistry are all as rapidly disseminated.

Several times during the Prince of Wales ceremony the words "via satellite" were flashed across the screen. How long did it take for the picture to travel between England and the U.S., and what route did it take?

The signals from Caernarvon Castle were sent directly to Goonhilly Downs, England's Intelsat Ground Station from which they were aimed at the new satellite now hovering 22,300 miles over the Indian Ocean, instead of the disabled Atlantic satellite. From it, the pictures and sound were beamed to Yamaguchi, Japan, and carried by land cable to Ibaraki, 90 miles south of Tokyo. From there they were beamed at the Pacific satellite, Intelsat III over the Equator, which tossed them to the U.S. Comsat Ground Station at Jamesburg, California, near the Monterey peninsula. From there they were trans-

mitted by microwave to the Canadian Broadcasting Corporation in Montreal for relay to New York to Hollywood and to San Francisco. Distance: 94,000 miles. Time: nine-tenths of a second! [53]

Communications networks are inherently global, and promise to become more so with the advent of communications satellites for telephone, radio, and television. . . . Involved are allocation of the electromagnetic spectrum, content of international television programs, standardization of codes and procedures, and many more. The role of the computer in association with international communications has yet to be defined, but appears certain to be a major one. Also of importance is the economic power of the large corporations specializing in the development and production of communications and computer hardware. . . .[54]

Swift global transportation carries around the world diverse products of mass production technology and provides common cultural artifacts which engender, in turn, shared attitudes in their requirements and use.

Ground transportation is already an international network in Europe and North America; similar networks are of increasing importance in Africa and South America. Air transportation is clearly global, with enormous problems of safety standards, prevention of dissemination of disease vectors, standardization of operational training, specialized international language and codes, procedures for international air shipment, security of air cargoes, international sales of aircraft and engines, and—most recently—the competitive development of three large supersonic transport aircraft.[55]

World tourism, as merely part of the increased mobility of man, shows an increase from 22 million international visitors in 1950 to approximately 100 million international visitors in 1968. The volume of such traffic and its influence on new ecological patterns of man may be gauged by the fact that in any 24-hour period in U.S. airspace alone there are approximately 25,000 persons aloft. For the world airspace, this figure would be about a quarter of a million persons each day off the surface of the earth.

Accompanying the diffusion of human service networks has been the almost invisible development of international regulatory agencies whose function and growth have been little interrupted by any of the surface wars and tensions:

1. The international postal union, which we all take for granted as a world public utility
2. The allocation of wavebands and frequencies for telecommunications
3. The regulation of air, sea, and other world transportation with elaborate codes of transnationally enforced codes and standards
4. The intricate network of world health agencies which monitor and control plague, smallpox, cholera, etc., on the global scale. In this network are a host of specialized centers operating in the transnational interest: international influenza

units headquartered in Britain and United States with 80 national units around the world, the Enteric Reference Laboratory in England which monitors world enteric disease, the World Health Serum bank's in various major countries, etc.

Agencies such as these, apprised of potential epidemic hazards to global health, can, potentially,

close a frontier, seal off a city, and even divert passenger and cargo flights in the air.

To these transnational regulatory agencies we may add the extraordinary growth of international meetings, conferences, and working projects. The first international congresses and meetings started only about 100 years ago. Today the annual average of such conferences runs to about 3,000 involving

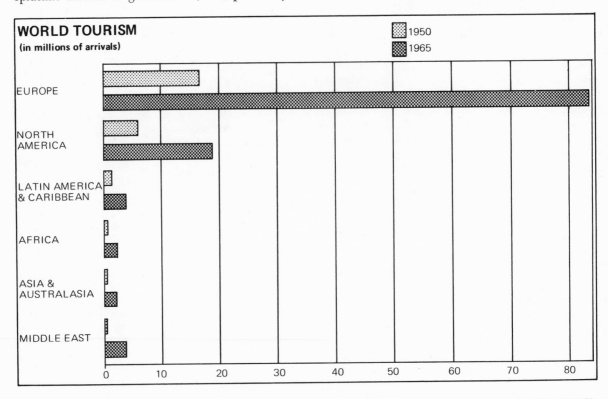

WORLD TOURISM
(in millions of arrivals)

1950
1965

EUROPE

NORTH AMERICA

LATIN AMERICA & CARIBBEAN

AFRICA

ASIA & AUSTRALASIA

MIDDLE EAST

0   10   20   30   40   50   60   70   80

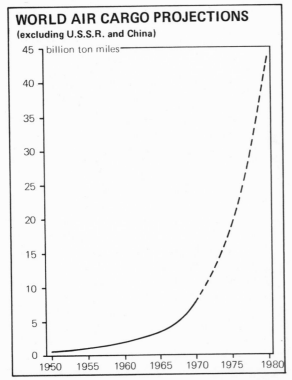

WORLD AIR CARGO PROJECTIONS
(excluding U.S.S.R. and China)

45 — billion ton miles
40
35
30
25
20
15
10
5
0

1950   1955   1960   1965   1970   1975   1980

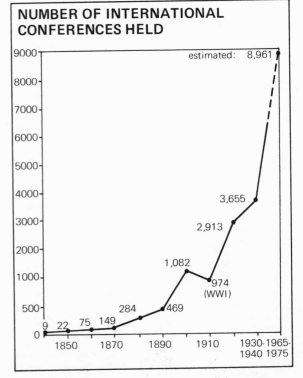

NUMBER OF INTERNATIONAL CONFERENCES HELD

9000   estimated: 8,961
8000
7000
6000
5000
4000   3,655
3000   2,913
2000
                    1,082
1000   974
                                (WWI)
500   284   469
    9 22 75 149
0
        1850   1870   1890   1910   1930- 1965-
                                    1940   1975

some two million active participants. The rise of international, professional, nongovernmental organizations parallels this: from approximately 1,000 in 1950 to 2,000 in 1960 and to almost 3,500 by 1968. These are only some of the growing invisible networks which now link the transnational society in myriad ways.

This introduces the role of the large transnational or multinational corporations. These are entities which are unprecedented by virtue of their size, global-diffused production, and relative autonomy from constraining national boundaries. They may use the capital of several nations, the territory of another group, and the labor force of still others.

During the 1970s, the non-Communist developing world will add some 500 million new consumers, although most of them will have low incomes. This growth will be equal to the combined population of Africa and Latin America in 1960. But even more important, there will be about 170 million additional entrants to the working age population—50 percent more than in the 1970s, when there was a worldwide growth in unemployment despite a five percent growth in output. If the rich countries are wise, they will help avoid this confrontation. How? One important measure would be for them to adjust their domestic economies to accommodate—and even take advantage of—a revolutionary change: namely, the rapid and recent trend toward internationalization of production, in which many countries contribute directly to the manufacture of a single industrial product. This development has been most notable so far in the electronics industry, with major components for products of American companies being manufactured in such diverse areas as Mexico, Korea, Taiwan, Hong Kong, Singapore, and Indonesia.[56]

The flexibility and power of (such) large international corporations now challenges the power of many nations. General Motors last year grossed 60 billion. This is larger than the total economy of Italy—and of 73 of the 120 member nations of the United Nations.

. . . (By virtue of their size and economic power) these international corporations play an increasingly dominant role in the world economy. They have international staff, international funding, international communication networks and—in the computer—even an international language.[57]

As another analyst has indicated . . . "of the 50 largest economic entities (in the world) 37 are countries and 13 are corporations. Of the top 100, 51 are corporations." [58] The growth rate of the top multinational corporations is nearly double that for four nation-states.

Such major corporations have direct influence over the core industries of even the major nations. Many decisions affecting the global economy now largely occur outside of the local national political system.

The nation-state today is, at best, a laggard partner in the global community, often contributing more to the disorder than the control of world

events, through clinging to its illusions of earlier physical and sovereign autonomy. In effect, though we continue to talk and act as though it were indeed possible, no single nation today, however large and powerful, can "go it alone." It cannot even wage war unilaterally without access to the cooperative networks of global technologies, materials, and services. And, paradoxically, as the latter grow in importance and become more complexly interdependent, they begin to militate against such disturbances.

While information can now be transmitted virtually instantaneously, to facilitate long-range bargaining, the time available for decision-making has decreased. The traditional conduct of secret, official diplomacy tends to be nullified by radio and television propaganda and by educational, cultural, and scientific exchanges. Swift transit of trouble-shooting negotiators to points of tension by air transport or for consultation with national leaders is counteracted by the ability of troublemakers and dissident groups to use these same means of travel.[59]

We may well reflect, in terms of real world control, that if all access to such transnationally sustained networks such as telecommunications, airlines, world weather, and health information, etc., were cut off, no developed nation could survive for more than a few days. This is amply illustrated in the disorder caused by even local power failures, airline strikes, and so on. It is also particularly noteworthy that in the recent Middle East hijackings, the one most powerful sanction which the international community was reluctant to employ was the withdrawal of air services to the disaffected nations!

Combating pollution will inevitably require international rather than national regulation as its starting point. First, pollution originating in a single nation-state might well spread through one of the components of the environment such as the air or oceans, into the territories of other nation-states. Secondly, in the context of current patterns for modernization of economies by the export from the most advanced countries of capital equipment for technological manufacturing, a plant which fails to contain adequate anti-polluting equipment will spread pollution by the very fact of its export. Thirdly, the measures to combat pollution need to be internationally prescribed and enforced for they will undoubtedly affect costs, and states which fail to observe them will gain a competitive advantage over those who do.[60]

These webs of international services and interlocked organizations represent a trend and commitment whose real effectiveness in asserting control over "runaway" world problems is not yet wholly realized. But there is a growing awareness that the path toward stable global integration lies via the strengthening of such transnational regulatory agencies.

TECHNOLOGICAL

We have characterized human psychosocial evolution as those overlays of parallel evolutionary forms through which human beings have partially sidestepped the natural genetic process of adaptation to the environment. In this process of "evolution-by-prothesis" we have not been forced to adapt our physical, or psychophysical characteristics more than has been strictly necessary. We have avoided having to grow longer legs, for speed and mobility, by inventing wheels; have chosen to make telescopes and microscopes rather than evolve larger and more powerful eyes, and have augmented the limited energies of the single individual through the cooperative energies of social organization and institutional systems of multi-individuals.

This augmentation of organic capacity is not confined to physical tools but includes also those "invisible" technologies which have as powerful an effect in modifying the environ to human purposes. Language, number, symbol, and image systems are also technological extensions of internal human processes which act directly upon the environ. The larger conceptual systems—philosophy, science, religion—are also evolved means of complexity, of reducing variability, and of extending human control.

In dealing with physical technology, we need to note the difference between preindustrial tool forms and specifically industrial tool forms. The former tended to single inventions locally operable by individuals or small groups and maintainable within the knowledge, limited energy, and material resource capacities of local regions, e.g., the sled, canoe, hammer, or plow. Industrial tools may be more specifically characterized as those which represent the coupling together of numbers of single tool forms into complex and large-scale systems which may not be wholly operated by individuals or small groups nor maintained by local resources alone, e.g., an airline, a telephone system, or a whole industry. They require the cooperative organizational energies of myriad individuals and access to the widest range of accumulated human knowledge and to the variety of energies and materials obtainable only at the global scale.

Most of the extraordinary evolution of these complex industrial tools has taken place in the last two hundred years. Though the process of technological development predates history, our present accelerations may be located as taking off toward the end of the eighteenth century with the steam engine. The brevity of this period probably accounts for the widespread apprehension that technological developments now threaten man, that technologies are out of control, etc.

Man has always assumed that an "evolving" technology would be of the mythological robotic variety, formed in his own image. It is, rather, more difficult to observe the evolution of the airplane from single person/single engine with multiple-wing surfaces, to multi-engine/single wing, to propellerless jets of enormous size, speed, and 400 passenger carrying capacity—almost in one human generation.

It is as difficult to equate the evolution of the family of "extended eyes"—from bulky, tripod, wetplate still cameras to microminiaturized television scanners spinning around the globe outside of the earth's atmosphere. We may better assess and control the further development of our technologies by applying to them some bio-evolutionary approach that we use in studying other life forms in the ecosystem.

As powered, renewed, and ultimately directed by human life, technology is as organic as a snail shell, a spiderweb, the carapace of a turtle, or an airborne dandelion seed. In many respects, it is now more ubiquitous as a functional component of the ecosystem than any other organic form except man himself.

The amounts of energy converted by machines; the materials extracted from the earth, processed, recombined, and redistributed in the technological metabolism; and the gross effects of such increased industrial metabolic rates on the ecosystem are now greater than the effects of many global populations of other organic species.

The industrial revolution, i.e., the large-scale application of inanimate machine energies to productive use, marks the point where humanity was potentially freed from the constraints of agriculturally based, marginal, survival societies to forms based on possible machine-produced abundance.

It is the point also, we may note, when there occurred the specific and critical interdependency of the various world regions—through improved communications and transportation, and the need for globally available materials and markets. This is a major characteristic of the world industrial process which tends to be ignored, i.e., "the peculiar interrelatedness that makes it impossible for certain countries to talk in terms of national economic growth". [61]

This industrial network interdependence also changes the character of the survival game. From this time on, no nation may go it alone in terms of self-sufficiency of energies, materials, or knowhow. The "survival game" is no longer a zero sum process in which participants compete fiercely for scarce resources which may be used autonomously and unilaterally: it is more clearly a non-zero sum game in which success and gain may only be predicated on the interdependent success of all players.

We hear much about the disintegrative effects of technological development in human affairs, but all too little emphasis is placed on the integrative

STAGES OF TECHNOLOGY

① Technological Revolutions

	Sub-stages / Notes
FIRST Technological revolution — The discovery and use of the wheel	Tusk, horn, and bone hand tools · All purpose stone & wood fist axes · Special purpose stone & wood hand tools
SECOND Technological Revolution — The discovery of methods for smelting ores and for making alloys and forged tools and weapons	Metal handtools with energy supplied by man and animals · Bronze · Iron Age
THIRD The Industrial Revolution	end of Franco-Prussian war
FOURTH Chemicals & Chemical Engineering	World War I
FIFTH Electrical Transmission & Telecommunications	World War II
SIXTH Transportation	controlled atomic fission
SEVENTH	

② Stages and Societies

AUTOMATION — STAGE V
MECHANIZATION — STAGE IV
DIVERSIFICATION — STAGE III
DOMESTICATION — STAGE II
ADAPTATION — STAGE I

DEVELOPED SOCIETIES — Industrial Economies

UNDERDEVELOPED SOCIETIES — Agriculturally Based Marginal Economies

Time scale: 10^6 · 5×10^5 · 10^4 · 5×10^4 · 5×10^3 · 2,000 BC · AD · 965 · 1,965 Years Before Present · 1965

THE LINE OF HIGH ADVANTAGE MOBILE ENVIRON CONTROL DEVELOPMENT WHICH GOES FROM SHIP, TO AIRPLANE, TO ROCKET, TO MANNED SPACE VEHICLE

MODE	Sailing Ships							Clippers	Steam Ships		Airplanes		Saturn V Rocket
TIME PERIOD	2,500 BC	500 BC	1,000 AD	1400	1500	1600	1700	1800	1900	1940	1940 Propeller	1950 Jet	1965
AVERAGE TONNAGE	150	250	30	300	100-500	1000	1,000	2,100	2,500	4,500	3,500	12,000	3,000 Tons
HORSE POWER	80	120	30-90	150-250	.....	500	750	.....	1,200	2,500	3,500	12,000	200,000 lbs. thrust
AVERAGE SPEED	8 knots	8 knots	12 knots	10 knots	10 knots	11 knots	12 knots	17-22 knots	16 knots	20 knots	300 m.p.h.	600 m.p.h.	25,000 m.p.h.

③ Dominant Ages

DOMINANT AGES	MODERN CRAFT 1,000 - 1784	MACHINE AGE 1785 - 1869	POWER AGE 1870 - 1952	ATOMIC AGE 1953 -
POWER	Human and Animal Muscle Wind and Water	Multiple Horse Teams and Steam Engines	Gasoline Engines and Electric Motors	Atomic Energy and Fossil Fuel Burning Equipment Used to Produce Electric Power and Heat - Fuel Cells
TOOLS	Hand Wrought Iron and Wooden	Machine Wrought Iron and Steel	Multiple Machine Tools and Automatic Machines	Cybernated Factories with Computer Closed Feedback Control Loops
WORK SKILLS	All-Around Skilled Craftsmen and Unskilled Manual Workers	Subdivided Manufacturing Processes Replace Skilled Craftsmen With Semiskilled Machine Operators	Human Feeder or Tender Replaced by Skilled Inspector - Mechanic	Highly Trained Engineer - Designers and-Skilled Maintenance Technician Systems Specialist and Programmer
MATERIALS	Wood, Iron and Bronze	Steel and Copper	Alloyed Steels, Light Alloys, and Aluminum	Plastics and Super Alloys (32 New Metals Used, Notably Magnesium and Titanium)
TRANSPORTATION	Walking, Use of Animals by Dirt Road or Via Waterways by Sailboat	Horse and Buggy, Steam Trains Via Steel Rails, and Steam Ships Via Ocean Ways	Automobile Via Paved Highways, Diesel Trains and Ships, and Airplane Via World Airways	Rocket and Jet Vertical Take Off Aircraft, Atomic Ships, Ground Effect Craft, Helicopters and Automobiles
COMMUNICATION	Word of Mouth, Drum, Smoke Signals, Messenger and Newspaper	Mail by Train and Ship, Mechanically Printed Newspaper, Telegraph, and Telephone	A.M. and F.M. Radio, Movies, Television, Magnetic Tape, Trans-ocean Telephone, and Microfilm	Video - Phone, Data Phone, Telstar & Syncom, World Wide Communication Satellites, 'Graphic' Computers

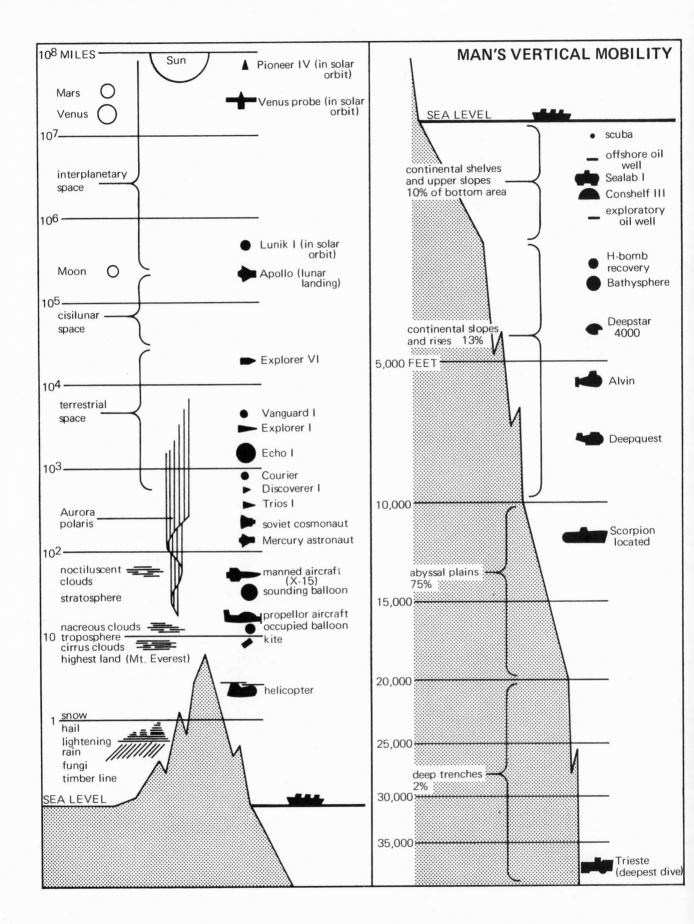

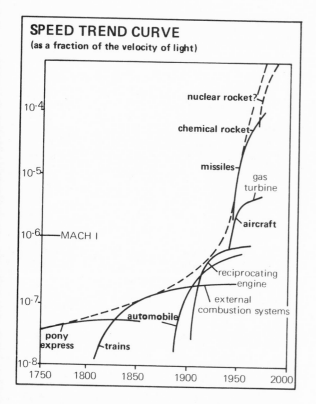

SPEED TREND CURVE
(as a fraction of the velocity of light)

nuclear rocket?

chemical rocket

missiles

gas turbine

aircraft

MACH I

reciprocating engine

external combustion systems

automobile

pony express

trains

force which the industrial network technologies now exert on a world scale.

The more advanced a technology or industry, the more pronounced its trend toward global service: airlines, telephones, and T.V. satellites are inherently global and minimally require world interlinkage and the widest availability of access for their efficient operation. The more customers, the more "economic" the service. The more global the technology, the more cooperatively integrative its operation must become, requiring similar institutional forms, attitudes, and organization for its maintenance and use.

As the production and consumption aspects of industrial technologies have gone global, they have, in turn, to be planned and managed increasingly on a worldwide basis, e.g., IBM's comment on the planning of a new computer: "Final specifications . . . reflect inputs from at least 20 countries around the world . . . so that it may meet the needs of virtually every market . . . handle decimal as well as sterling . . . print output not only in Indian, or Japanese Katakana but in typefaces for any of 22 different languages."

To such specifications, we may add the locally trained and internationally exchanged technicians, equipment, standard instructions, and programs—plus the fact that the manufacture and assembly of various components may be thousands of miles apart.

The emphasis on such "integrative" aspects is not to suggest that we do not need to assess more consciously and plan more deliberately our technological development. Indeed, the more pervasive

the effects and the larger the scale of impacts of specific technological and industrial developments for larger numbers of people, the more we have to deal consciously with a process which up until now has been allowed to proceed in piecemeal and haphazard fashion. Such assessment, planning, and forecasting requires clear information about the changes in the intrinsic nature of technological evolution so that it is not wholly based upon technical, economic, or national cost/benefit criteria.

Our current techno-economic models for such assessment, in general, are still biased with pre-industrial premises. One specifically weak aspect is the nature of wealth-goods-use value. Preindustrially, the "marginal survival" indicators of land, labor, and artifacts represented wealth. Later it compressed to "capital," functioning as the exchange vehicle for traditional wealth inputs and outputs in the economy. With industrialized mass production, such traditional indicators became obsolete in terms of wealth-goods produced by the machine. For the first time, we could produce utility objects in huge numbers with a precision and uselife greater than any produced previously, in a fraction of the time, and with swiftly decreasing investment of human energy. Availability and use became separated from "value."

When manufacturing technologies went over into the invisible ranges of electrical and other radiation energies, this further separated use from intrinsic "wealth" value. For example, the electric light bulb, the telephone, and computer terminal are only contact units for "coupled" access to other systems and have little or no intrinsic value apart from their direct human-use function. Many such products are now typically expendable after a single or multiple-use cycle, and the materials from which they are made are increasingly recycled in a variety of product configurations.

With the entry of cybernetic control into the industrial process, direct human-labor input in production has even less relevance to economic growth; industrial productivity itself loses its main role as a primary society activity as society moves farther from marginal survival for most toward possible material abundance for all its members. In fully automated production, the basic (wealth) resource input is information-programming-machine performance. The machines and, increasingly, the material resources forming them and their products are "produced" by other information inputs and recycled and restructured through further information. The only nonexpendable and "value" component in the whole process is man with his organized and accumulated knowledge, and his role of defining the value of the activity by the degree to which it assists or constrains his human functions.

Our conceptual "accounting" models are still agriculturally oriented with emphasis on sequentially limited, material, visible exchanges of goods while the major services which now more pervasively maintain society operate indirect, non-linear, and non-sequential exchanges whose major component is increasingly "information." Other characteristics now inherent in emergent postindustrial technological forms include:

1. increases in energy conversion efficiencies.
2. increases in performance per unit of materials and energies invested.
3. increases in component performance reliability.
4. increase of miniaturization; i.e., the progressive reductions in size, weight, operatng, and maintenance energies.
5. decrease in overall operating economy, unit costs in direct ratio to increased usage and more universal access.

We may note that while most accounting, assessment, and conceptual control models of techno-economic efficiency are still based on the materially visible relative static inventories of input and output, all the major trends in advanced technologies are increasingly "subvisible" and tend toward increased ephemeralization.

These organic-developmental trends in technology are most strikingly evident since the introduction of cybernetics (significantly, and symbolically, derived from the word for "steering" in the navigational sense). Defined as the mechanization of sensory thought and other psychophysical processes, cybernetics is an extension of the control capacities of the human nervous system into electromechanical devices.

We may underline its importance in socio-ecological terms. As the mechanical and chemical energy converters of the first series of industrial revolutions freed human muscle from routine tasks, so the computer revolution potentially frees man from comparable routine "intellectual" tasks such as monitoring, supervising, and controlling many simultaneous and complex technical processes. Also, and importantly, it gives the possibility of swiftly expanding our global production, distribution, and logistical support services toward satisfying the urgent material needs of large numbers of human beings still on the edge of survival.

In the field of computers, which are widely considered "among the most significant indicators of the new technology," the United States has installed 56,000 compared with 20,000 in Western Europe, 5,500 in the Soviet Union, and 6,000 in Japan. "A look ahead to the late 1970s is instructive, when the United States will have about 100,000 of a world total of 215,000 computers, Western Europe, 50,000; the U.S.S.R., 35,000; Japan, 20,000; and the remaining three-quarters of the world only 10,000." [62]

Some computer performance characteristics:

Weight, Volume, Power Costs: In 1953 a computer weighed approximately 5,000 pounds, occupied 300-400 cubic feet and required 40 kilowatts of power. Today's computer weights approximately 50 pounds, is a thousand times smaller and uses 265% less power than the 1953 model.

In 1945 (at a labor cost of $1.00/hour and at rate of 16 operations per minute) it cost about $1,000 to do a million operations on a keyboard and took at least a month. Today, computers can do a million operations for less than six cents. By 1975 this is estimated at less than 6/10 of a cent.

WORLD COMPUTER POPULATION

NUMBER OF COMPUTERS PER MILLION INHABITANTS (1970)

	Number per million	TOTAL NUMBER OF COMPUTERS
WORLD	29	106,000
UNITED STATES	299	62,500
CANADA	140	3,000
WEST GERMANY	105	6,100
UNITED KINGDOM	105	5,900
FRANCE	88	4,500
NETHERLANDS	84	1,100
SCANDINAVIA	69	1,500
JAPAN	57	5,900
ITALY	50	2,700
EAST GERMANY	30	500
U.S.S.R.	22	5,500
CZECHOSLOVAKIA	13	200
POLAND	12	420
YUGOSLAVIA	8	180
ROMANIA	2	50

0   100   200   300

REGIONAL COMPUTER POPULATION

UNITED STATES	62,500
WESTERN EUROPE	24,000
U.S.S.R.	5,500
EASTERN EUROPE	1,500
OTHER	12,500
WORLD TOTAL	106,000

The economic value of human operations is now reduced by factor of 10, i.e., the value of uniquely human operations (thinking) at a computational level changed by factor of 10.

(A) Storage Size: From 1955-65 the storage size of central processing computer unit (cpu) decreased by a factor of ten. During the next decade, fully integrated circuits begin to reduce this size by a factor of about 1000.

(B) Storage Speed: From 1955-65 internal speeds have increased by a factor of 200 and by 1975 such speeds are expected to again increase by this amount.

(C) Storage Cost: During the first decade of the computer the cost of performing one million operations decreased from $10.00 to about 5 cents. By 1975 it is estimated that this decrease will amount to an additional factor of about 300.

(D) Computer Power: The total installed computer power in the United States during 1955 had a capacity of about one-half million additions per second. By 1965 this capacity increased to 200 million per second and if growth rates are sustained through 1975, the increase in capability will be about 400 fold.[63]

The cybernetic revolution has occurred largely within the past two decades. It is important to underline this and to recognize its evolutionary significance. We sense this period of change and transition as one of the most critical in human history. The specific focus of our discussion centers around our capacity to control the enormous scale of our present global undertakings in a more positive, efficient, and naturally advantageous manner and to avoid the dislocations and dangerous side effects of out swiftly accelerating technological growth.

It is of key relevance, therefore, that cybernetics is also specifically developed for massive control and decision-making in handling large-scale systems with many complex and variable factors. At the point then, where man's affairs reach the scale of potential disruption of the global ecosystem, he invents, with seeming spontaneity, precisely those conceptual and physical technologies which enable him to deal with the magnitude of a complex planetary society.

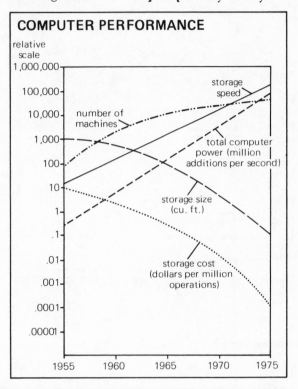

COMPUTER PERFORMANCE

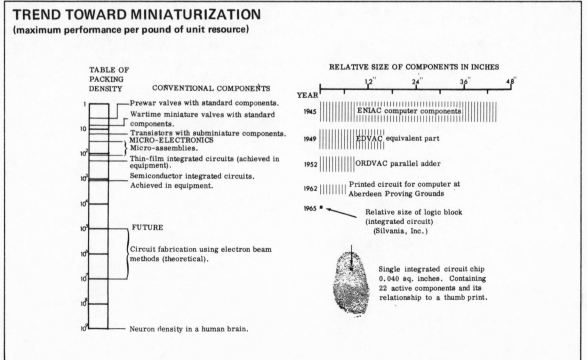

TREND TOWARD MINIATURIZATION
(maximum performance per pound of unit resource)

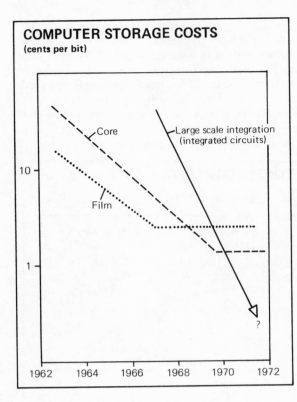

COMPUTER STORAGE COSTS
(cents per bit)

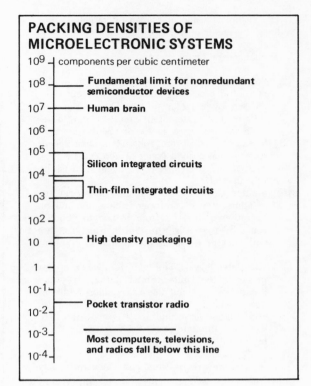

PACKING DENSITIES OF MICROELECTRONIC SYSTEMS

10^9 — components per cubic centimeter

10^8 — **Fundamental limit for nonredundant semiconductor devices**

10^7 — **Human brain**

10^6

10^5 — **Silicon integrated circuits**

10^4

10^3 — **Thin-film integrated circuits**

10^2

10 — **High density packaging**

1

10^{-1} — **Pocket transistor radio**

10^{-2}

10^{-3} — **Most computers, televisions, and radios fall below this line**

10^{-4}

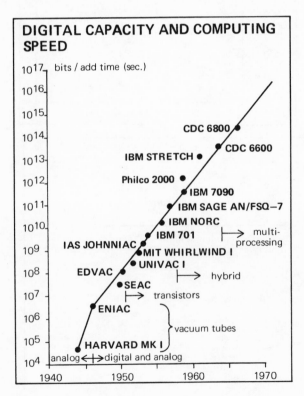

DIGITAL CAPACITY AND COMPUTING SPEED

10^{17} — bits / add time (sec.)

The point reached recently (when such systems began to be combined with the remote sensing, earth monitoring, and potential environ control capacities of the orbiting satellite) marks the extension of this symbiosis to include the entire planetary ecology.

On earth, the most pervasive aspect has been the growing automation of production, services, and information flow in the advanced economies. The extent to which such automated systems begin to assume the operation of the externalized metabolic systems of such economies is far-reaching. Apart from automated factories and continentally linked automatic inventory, dispatch, and other control operations, the whole energy conversion, transmission and distribution system is increasingly under automated control. The intercontinental telephone linkage systems, airline reservations, flight path control, etc., are other examples.

The most extraordinary developments of this biotic extension may lie with the growth of orbital satellite capacity. These are, in a very real sense the prime ecological tools of the future through which we may adjust our activities more harmoniously within the biosphere.

The United States had 302 earth-orbiting satellites in space on January 1, the Air Force reports.

The Soviet Union had only 102 such craft in orbit.

The United States also had 18 deep-space probes circling the sun; the Soviet Union had 15.

Since the first earth satellite, Sputnik I, was launched on October 4, 1957, 4,842 objects of all kinds have been placed in space—including 2,114 that remain in space and 2,728 that have decayed.[64]

A NEW SYMBIOSIS. As in our natural symbiotic relations with plants and animals, our relationship to our industrial network and particularly with our cybernetic systems, has been subtly changing toward a more closely woven organic interdependence.

In addition to conventional photography from satellites, multispectral sensing is being employed with the infrared, ultraviolet, and other wavelengths, such as x-ray and radar. Using infrared, for example, it would be possible to have detailed surveys of traffic in and out of cities, of human occupancy of buildings through heat patterns. Numbers of cattle on grazing range, changes in forests, fields, and even animal and bird migrations could be easily surveyed.

This combination of resource mapping, crop and livestock pattern changes, and weather-cycle monitoring can be of inestimable value to the developing countries, especially where it bypasses the lack of specialists and technical personnel to do this work at ground level. In many cases, resource inventories which might otherwise take decades of large-scale human and technical energies may be accomplished in a few months.

(One) can foresee the possibility that the techniques for remote sensing will evolve into a highly automatic operation, in which an unmanned satellite orbiting the earth will carry multiband sensing equipment together with a computer. Thus equipped the satellite could, for any particular area, take inventory of the resources and produce a printout that would amount to a resource map of the area. The computer could then use the inventory data in conjunction with preprogrammed (i.e., human requirements) factors and could reach a decision for the optimum management of the area.[65]

Besides these potential future advantages, present augmentation of our air, water, and soil pollution, whose magnitudes seemed just about to slip beyond

human grasp, may now be subject to our direct assessment and within our anticipatory control.

The use of such satellite systems for more direct human communication is already far advanced. The first recorded voice was heard from a satellite only twelve years ago, four years later the first live telephone, television, data and facsimile transmissions were made between Europe and the United States via Telestar I and II. Since then various new satellite relays have transmitted between Russia, Japan, the United States and Europe.

Such communication has become a fundamental part of our society; three operational systems have come into being: the Intelsat, the Department of Defense series, and the Soviet Molnivas.

At the end of the decade the possibilities for relay from satellite to home or individual have become the next useful and logical step.[66]

The same may be said for satellite-relayed education, which can bring all or any of these communicative modes to bear on the deployment of educational services anywhere in the world. But here one must say that so far the results in the advanced countries of airborne TV broadcasts and the interlinkage of television, computers, and other systems connecting educational institutions have not been spectacular. As in other areas of the application of advanced technological means to traditional social processes, the tendency is to try to convey the old content in the new channels.

Each technical advance poses a new challenge toward reconceptualizing and transforming the process in which it is used. If this challenge is not recognized, the added technique may even be a retrograde step. At present, much of our educational technology is being used in wholly negative fashion. Rather than enhancing and expanding education—by refashioning its content, decentralizing its means, and allowing for more personalized instruction and more time for human interaction—new techniques are merely superimposed upon a largely obsolete system in a manner that perpetuates its malpractice in more repetitive and more bureaucratic forms.

It is worth restating at every opportunity that the negatives of our present situation are not in the technological revolutions as such, but in the conceptual approaches and social attitudes that determine how new technical means will be employed. We are the active instruments that create a technological passivity.

ENERGY. The vast increase in the amounts of energy required to sustain our present levels of productivity and the necessary augmentation of such levels to accommodate even more people, at higher standards of living, leads to questions of the most efficient types of energy conversion, transmission, and process uses.

Also pertinent to the crucial role of energy resources in sustaining our present economies is

INSTRUMENTATION POTENTIALLY REQUIRED OF EARTH RESOURCES SURVEYS

SENSOR	SAMPLE APPLICATIONS
	AGRICULTURE AND FORESTRY PRODUCTION
Metric camera Panoramic camera Multispectral tracking telescope Multiband synoptic camera	Gather data on plant vigor and disease in order to aid in the increase of agriculture and forest production.
Radar imager Radar altimeter/scatterometer Wide range spectral scanner IR radiometer/spectrometer	GEOGRAPHY, CARTOGRAPHY, CULTURAL RESOURCE Gather data to permit better use of rural and metropolitan land areas and to update topographic base maps and census inventories.
Microwave imager Microwave radiometer Laser altimeter/scatterometer	GEOLOGY AND MINERAL RESOURCES Gather data to aid in (1) the discovery and exploitation of mineral and petroleum resources; (2) the prediction of natural disasters.
Ultraviolet spectrometer imager	HYDROLOGY AND WATER RESOURCES
Radio frequency reflectivity Absorption spectroscopy Magnetometer Gravity gradiometer Viewfinder[1] Earth-based sensors[2] Advanced TV system	Gather data to aid in the location and better usage of water resources. OCEANOGRAPHY Gather data to aid in ocean transportation and to aid in more efficient utilization of fisheries.

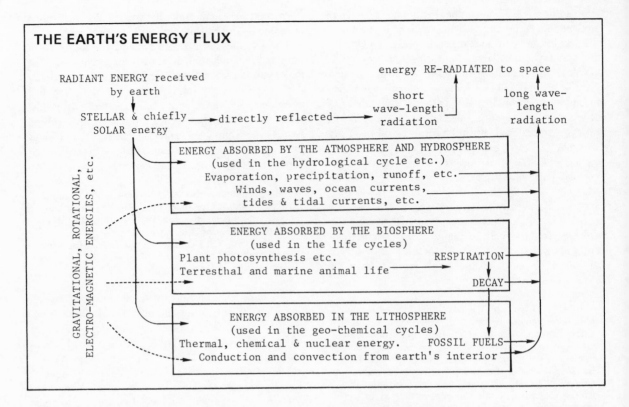

THE EARTH'S ENERGY FLUX

RADIANT ENERGY received by earth

STELLAR & chiefly SOLAR energy

GRAVITATIONAL, ROTATIONAL, ELECTRO-MAGNETIC ENERGIES, etc.

energy RE-RADIATED to space

directly reflected → short wave-length radiation   long wave-length radiation

ENERGY ABSORBED BY THE ATMOSPHERE AND HYDROSPHERE
(used in the hydrological cycle etc.)
Evaporation, precipitation, runoff, etc.
Winds, waves, ocean currents,
tides & tidal currents, etc.

ENERGY ABSORBED BY THE BIOSPHERE
(used in the life cycles)
Plant photosynthesis etc.   RESPIRATION
Terresthal and marine animal life   DECAY

ENERGY ABSORBED IN THE LITHOSPHERE
(used in the geo-chemical cycles)
Thermal, chemical & nuclear energy.   FOSSIL FUELS
Conduction and convection from earth's interior

the rate at which we have consumed such resources in the recent brief period, for example:

> . . . although coal has been mined for about 800 years, one-half of the coal produced during that period has been mined during the last 31 years. Half of the world's cumulative production of petroleum has occurred during the 12 years period since 1956 . . . in brief, most of the world's consumption of energy from the fossil fuels during its entire history has occurred during the last 25 years.[67]

The amounts required in the immediate and long-range future call into question certain preferential uses of specific fuels and the more economic conservation of others, not only in terms of our actual energy supply and potential reserves but also in terms of the by-product pollutants of the various sources.

First, we should consider the overall supply of energy to the ecosystem. The prime sources are radiant energy from the sun, the kinetic and potential energy of the earth's gravitational system, and energy that is radiated from the interior of the earth. Of these, our central focus is on solar energy. Gravitational energy enters into all energy transactions on the earth surface, but is considered less of a direct source than its secondary derivatives of water and tidal power. The interior earth energies, geothermal, have not been used on a large scale so far.

To these three main sources, we might add those energies accruing from the earth's spin and atmospheric circulation: wind energies and differences in temperature and pressure related to climatic change. However, these are less important now than in former periods.

In addition to the organic process of solar energy storage in fossil fuels, we should also consider the material mass of the earth itself as representing a vast store of cosmic energies locked in a myriad of chemical combinations from the major geological periods of the earth's physical formation. The biomass, that is, the entire complex of all life forms on earth, also represents a long and continuous impounding process of solar energies.

We have, thus, a division into stored or "capital" energies such as the fossil fuels and fissionable elements in the earth's crust, and those energies in constantly renewed "income" from solar radiation and other sources.

Capital energies or, the stored, unrenewable energy deposits in the earth include:

1. fossil fuels: coal, natural gas, oil (including shale and oil sands).
2. nuclear fuels: those elements which may yield energy through nuclear fission and fusion processes.

The main fossil fuel deposits have been built up over a 500 million year geological time period. Their presently prodigal use, with its many deleterious by-products effects, suggests that we review such usages with care in that they do represent a convenient and accessible form of stored energy which could be used now, or in the future, in many different, much more economical and intelligent ways. Nuclear fuels, available from the fission of heavy element isotopes and the fusion of lighter

Energy Conversion (naturally occurring) | **Energy Conversion (human agencies)** | **Merits** | **Demerits** | **Human Utilization**

Income Energies — Continuous or renewable energy receipts of light, heat, gravity, cosmic rays, etc.

Stellar Energy Sources Chiefly Solar

Indirect Inanimate — Molecular movement (temperature differences between atmosphere, earth & ocean), geothermal heat & tidal forces.
- Sails, waterwheels, wind generators, hydro-electric generators, drying processes, geo-thermal steam & tidal power facilities
- Merits: Winds, temperature differences geothermal heat etc. are continuous & have few inherent pollutants
- Demerits: Difficulty of controls, periodic surges, geographic disproportion etc.

Indirect Animate — Photosynthesis, microbial energy conversion.
- Food, human labor, draft animals, fermentation & alcohol extraction from vegetation, wood fuels, dung, etc. controlled microbial action in agri-industrial processes.
- Merits: Self regenerating systems. Microbial action may be used in waste reclamation cycle.
- Demerits: Large volumes of heat energy dissipated in direct metabolic processes.

Direct — Photo-Chemical, Photo-electrical, Thermo-electrical.
- Heat and electrical energy yielded through electro-chemical reactions & optical concentrations of lights, etc.
- Merits: Direct energy transfer, may be stored bio-chemically or electro-chemically but on a relatively small scale.
- Demerits: Presently not capable of economic application on wide scale or large volume range.

Human Utilization: Cooling food, preserving food, cooking food, space heating, space cooling, pumping water, air & gasses, motive power, lighting, communications, industrial heating, conversion and forming of materials, etc.

Capital Energies — Exhaustible or unrenewable energy sources stored over extended periods of time.

Fossil Fuels — Coal, petroleum, natural gas, shale oil, tar sands, etc.
- Heat and electrical energy yielded through combustion in various chemical processes and mechanisms
- Merits: May be stored, transported and controlled with ease and in large volumes.
- Demerits: Excess waste heat, gasses, & pollutents effect biogeochemical processes.

Fissile Fuels — Radioactive fissionable elements.
- Heat and electrical energy yielded through acceleration of atoms in combination with electro-mechanical systems.
- Merits: Independent of geography, minimal upkeep, by-product wastes may be used as other fuels.
- Demerits: Large investment in sheailding and fuel refinement, disposal of radio-active waste is a present key problem.

Bio-geochemical — Cycling minerals such as nitrates, phosphates, etc.
- Heat yielded through chemical reactions, etc.
- Merits: May be stored, controlled, and used as fertilizers in other food energy processes etc.
- Demerits: Used in explosives etc. Primarily destructive energy use.

DEVELOPING ENERGY SYSTEMS

- Controlled thermonuclear fusion
- Fast breeder reactors
- Magneto-hydrodynamic generators(MHD)
- Thermionics
- Thermo-electricity
- Direct conversion of solar energy
- Shale-oil & tar-sands
- Coal liquification & gasification
- Fuel cells & bio-chemical energy
- Aerogenerators
- Geothermal energy
- Tidal energy

PROVEN ENERGY SYSTEMS

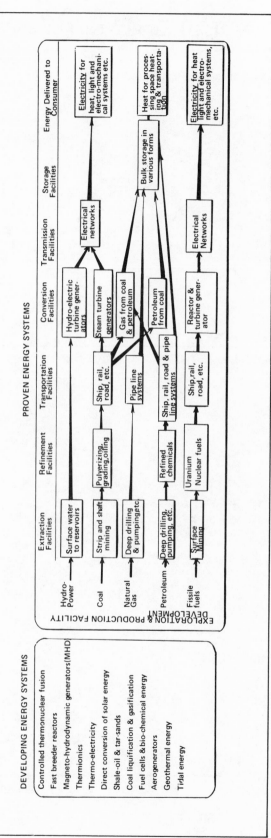

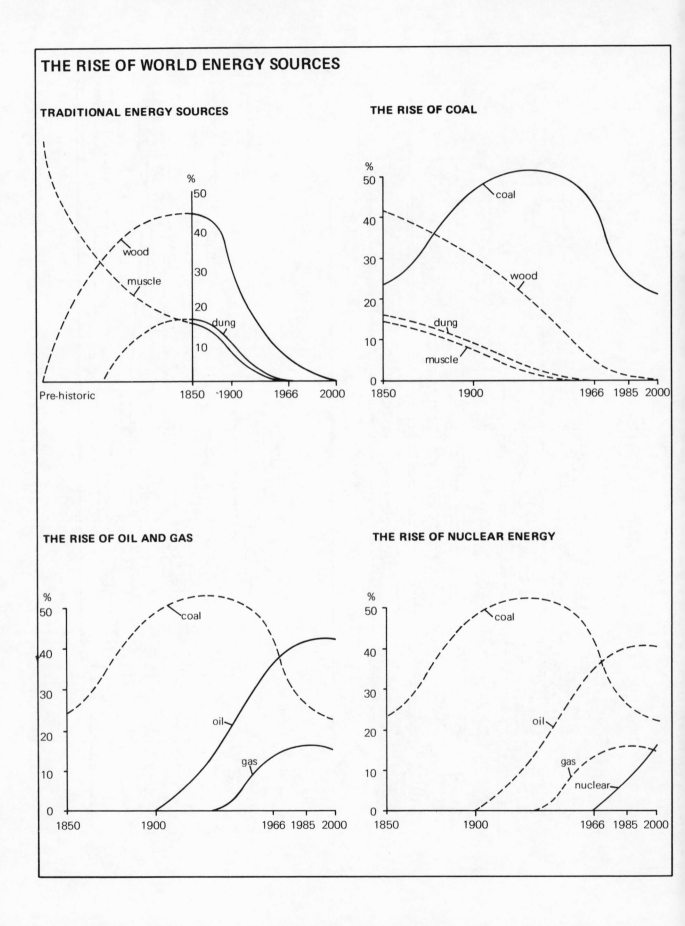

THE RISE OF WORLD ENERGY SOURCES

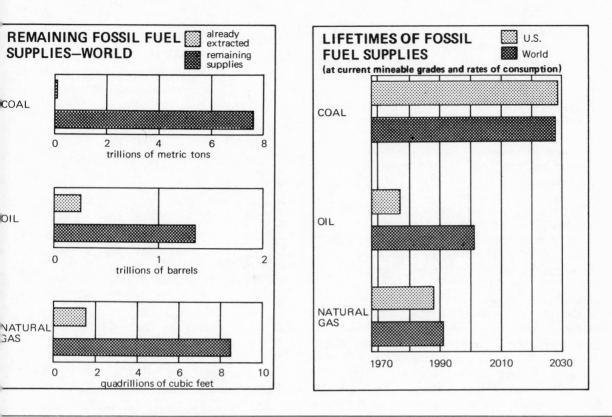

REMAINING FOSSIL FUEL SUPPLIES—WORLD

already extracted
remaining supplies

COAL

0   2   4   6   8
trillions of metric tons

OIL

0   1   2
trillions of barrels

NATURAL GAS

0   2   4   6   8   10
quadrillions of cubic feet

LIFETIMES OF FOSSIL FUEL SUPPLIES
(at current mineable grades and rates of consumption)

U.S.
World

COAL

OIL

NATURAL GAS

1970   1990   2010   2030

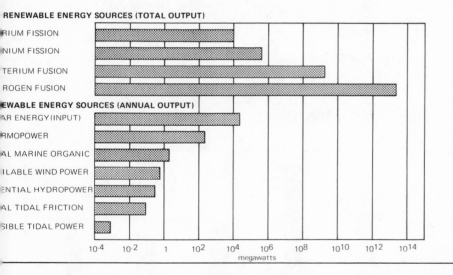

POTENTIAL MARINE ENERGY SOURCES

NON-RENEWABLE ENERGY SOURCES (TOTAL OUTPUT)

THORIUM FISSION
URANIUM FISSION
DEUTERIUM FUSION
HYDROGEN FUSION

RENEWABLE ENERGY SOURCES (ANNUAL OUTPUT)

SOLAR ENERGY (INPUT)
THERMOPOWER
TOTAL MARINE ORGANIC
AVAILABLE WIND POWER
POTENTIAL HYDROPOWER
TOTAL TIDAL FRICTION
FEASIBLE TIDAL POWER

10^{-4} 10^{-2} 1 10^2 10^4 10^6 10^8 10^{10} 10^{12} 10^{14}
megawatts

" ... the sea harbors far more non-renewable energy than the land, in the form of the potential fusion energy of its hydrogen and deuterium.

"The power demand of the world in 2000 has been projected as 14 million megawatts .... the ultimate fission and fusion of energy content of the oceans is shown in terms of multiples of that anticipated annual demand.

"Thorium and uranium fission could, in principle, supply this 1.4×10^7 MW for some 700,000 years, whereas deuterium and hydrogen fusion can sypply it for times that are greater than the age of the solar svstem. Although terrestrial sources of fissionable materials are probably greater (and more economical) than the marine, the sea is clearly the predominant source of fusible deuterium and hydrogen.

"Feasible tidal power can supply a tenth of one percent of the total need, but even the entire tidal dissipation in all the oceans of the world represents only ten percent of the total need." – Robert Colbarn, ed.

elements, though extensible toward an income energy resource through profusion of materials, are presently limited by various factors including the disposal of their by-product wastes.

Income energies are the naturally recurring energies available to man by tapping into the regenerative cycles in the ecosystem and include:

1. photosynthesis: we have hitherto considered this energy conversion process only in its food energy cycling role. There are many other ways in which energy may be directly extracted from vegetation product cycles; e.g., through fuels

from wood and other sources; by microbial action in "biological fuel cells," etc.

2. other direct solar energy uses: through concentrating lenses and reflectors into cooling devices; through photoelectrical and photochemical fuel cells, etc.

3. hydrological: as derived from the earth's gravitational system through rivers, dams, etc., and the direct use of tidal and wave power; also various modes of tapping into the hydrological cycle of evaporation precipitation.

4. wind: though this is intermittent and variable,

improvements in storage capacities may enable this source to be more widely used.

5. temperature: temperature differentials between atmospheric and earth/water surfaces yield energy potentials of considerable magnitude.

6. geothermal: tapping directly into the heat of the earth either through naturally occurring volcanic sources of hot gases and water or by drilling artificial vents for similar purposes.

7. other "unconventional" sources: magnetophydrodynamics, thermionics, etc.

The income energies summarily noted above, have fewer demerits than any of the capital energy sources in terms of pollutant by-products and other noxious side effects to humans, or as yet ascertained effects on the overall function of the ecological system. Apart from being "cleaner" energy sources, they are also potentially inexhaustible as renewed by the sun, or as occurring in the naturally cyclic ecosystem's operation. In terms of environ redesign they afford many experimental and innovative directions which are relatively unexplored through our overdependence on the fossil fuels. Aerospace technologies have already given considerable lead here in the utilization of self-powered communications and other systems dependent on fuel cells of different types.

The advantages of nuclear energy for the underdeveloped regions of the world are:

It can function anywhere. It is independent of geography, climate, and the general cultural level of the inhabitants. Upkeep is minimal . . . Needed amounts of nuclear fuel are easily transported, and

PROJECTION OF MAJOR NUCLEAR POWER PROGRAMS TO 1976	TOTAL POWER (in megawatts)	NUMBER OF STATIONS
UNITED STATES	76,500	107
UNITED KINGDOM	13,000	42
WEST GERMANY	10,000	25
JAPAN	9,500	19
U.S.S.R.	8,800	29
SWEDEN	5,400	10
CANADA	4,000	9
FRANCE	3,000	11
SPAIN	2,600	6
SWITZERLAND	2,250	5
BELGIUM	1,500	4
ITALY	1,400	5
INDIA	1,200	6
NETHERLANDS	1,000	3
BULGARIA	800	2
ARGENTINA	600	2
MEXICO	600	1
AUSTRALIA	500	1
BRAZIL	500	1
NORWAY	500	1
GREECE	450	1
FINLAND	440	1
AUSTRIA	400	1
PAKISTAN	325	2
THAILAND	300	1
CZECHOSLOVAKIA	100	1
TOTAL	**145,665**	**296**

the consumed weight is negligible. Operation is automatic and can be managed by a limited personnel. And because initial costs are high (and nuclear fuels are and will remain government property), installations will continue to be planned and financed by national or multinational agencies. They can, therefore, be placed where they are needed.[68]

The present disadvantages of nuclear energies, of course, lie in the fission process, in which,

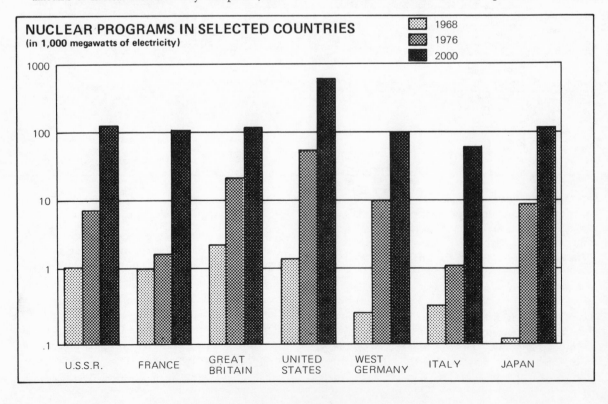

NUCLEAR PROGRAMS IN SELECTED COUNTRIES
(in 1,000 megawatts of electricity)

1968
1976
2000

U.S.S.R.   FRANCE   GREAT BRITAIN   UNITED STATES   WEST GERMANY   ITALY   JAPAN

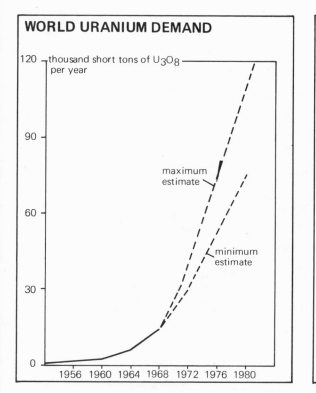

WORLD URANIUM DEMAND

120 — thousand short tons of U₃O₈ per year

maximum estimate

minimum estimate

1956 1960 1964 1968 1972 1976 1980

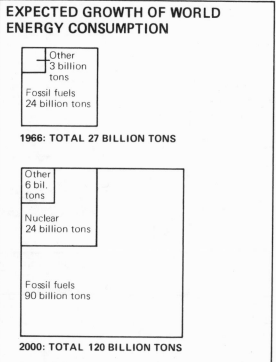

EXPECTED GROWTH OF WORLD ENERGY CONSUMPTION

Other 3 billion tons

Fossil fuels 24 billion tons

1966: TOTAL 27 BILLION TONS

Other 6 bil. tons

Nuclear 24 billion tons

Fossil fuels 90 billion tons

2000: TOTAL 120 BILLION TONS

though the fuel is unconventional, the ways in which energy is converted in the generating plants is relatively conventional. There are also the growing problems of atomic waste disposal, "seepage" of radioactivity, thermal discharges, etc.

International transfer of electric power is of no great consequence but the transfer of power technology—particularly atomic power—is of wide international concern. Control of the facilities, the fuel, and the processing of spent fuel elements are all international problems. Supplies of coal, natural gas, petroleum, and other fossil fuels are not uniformly distributed among the nations of the world and raise questions of international adjustment and accommodation. The global problems of air pollution and disposal of radioactive materials are also closely related to power generation.[69]

Our major problems are: how to maintain our present level of energy consumption with its undue reliance on the fossil fuels and how to increase and redistribute the availability of world energy so as to aid the lesser developed "energy poor" nations. This will require multiple efforts in research and development in two main areas: the generation of energy (source, mode of energy conversion, etc.) and energy conversion efficiencies (both in prime generation and in end uses). Many of our end-use processes are operating at extremely low and wasteful levels of efficiency: the transmission, storage, and distribution of energy, again, are areas into which less research and development have been directed than should have been the case.

The production of world energy (which parallels, but does not exactly match consumption figures

due to various indirect uses, losses in transmission, etc.) has increased at the average rate of 3¾ percent annually from 1860 to 1958 and has had various growth periods when levels rose above five to six percent.

From 1958 to 1961 this annual increase rate has risen considerably. The world's consumption of industrial energy from all sources increased by approximately 19 percent during the period 1961 to 1964. This was an unprecedented rise to a new level which has been sustained: the higher increase in the present years is due to population rise and the rate of industrialization of underdeveloped regions.

Nuclear energy is the only new source that is currently expected to make a large contribution to satisfying energy needs during the next twenty years or so. The fast breeder reactors that should come into commercial operation in the later 1970s will eventually breed as much fuel as they consume, which will contribute to the expected fall in costs.

Although both oil and natural gas will probably pass their peak in terms of market shares before the year 2000, output of these fuels will continue to rise in absolute terms as total world-energy demand—now growing at about 5 percent a year—continues to expand.[70]

. . . Last year the United States used about 500 million tons of bituminous coal, about 19 trillion cubic feet of natural gas, about 5 billion barrels of petroleum, and about 3,000 tons of uranium. The Department of the Interior projections for the year 2000 indicate that the demand for bituminous coal will probably quadruple, that for natural gas will at least triple, for petroleum more than double, and for uranium will most likely be 20 times greater. For only one of these sources of energy—bituminous coal

WORLD ENERGY FLOW—1964

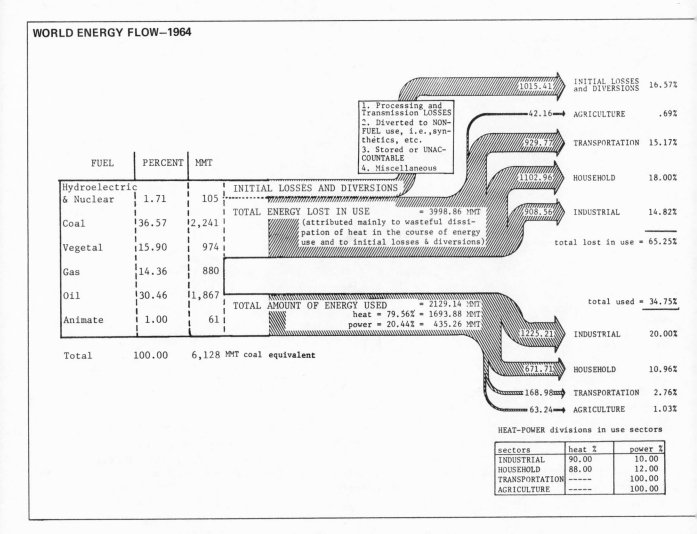

FUEL	PERCENT	MMT
Hydroelectric & Nuclear	1.71	105
Coal	36.57	2,241
Vegetal	15.90	974
Gas	14.36	880
Oil	30.46	1,867
Animate	1.00	61
Total	100.00	6,128 MMT coal equivalent

1. Processing and Transmission LOSSES
2. Diverted to NON-FUEL use, i.e., synthetics, etc.
3. Stored or UNACCOUNTABLE
4. Miscellaneous

INITIAL LOSSES AND DIVERSIONS

TOTAL ENERGY LOST IN USE   = 3998.86 MMT
(attributed mainly to wasteful dissipation of heat in the course of energy use and to initial losses & diversions)

TOTAL AMOUNT OF ENERGY USED   = 2129.14 MMT
heat = 79.56% = 1693.88 MMT
power = 20.44% = 435.26 MMT

1015.41	INITIAL LOSSES and DIVERSIONS	16.57%
42.16	AGRICULTURE	.69%
929.77	TRANSPORTATION	15.17%
1102.96	HOUSEHOLD	18.00%
908.56	INDUSTRIAL	14.82%
	total lost in use =	65.25%
	total used =	34.75%
1225.21	INDUSTRIAL	20.00%
671.71	HOUSEHOLD	10.96%
168.98	TRANSPORTATION	2.76%
63.24	AGRICULTURE	1.03%

HEAT-POWER divisions in use sectors

sectors	heat %	power %
INDUSTRIAL	90.00	10.00
HOUSEHOLD	88.00	12.00
TRANSPORTATION	-----	100.00
AGRICULTURE	-----	100.00

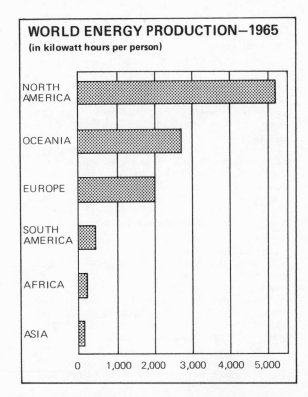

WORLD ENERGY PRODUCTION—1965
(in kilowatt hours per person)

NORTH AMERICA
OCEANIA
EUROPE
SOUTH AMERICA
AFRICA
ASIA

0   1,000 2,000 3,000 4,000 5,000

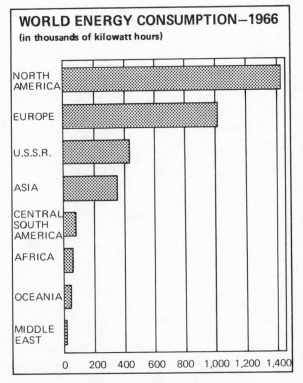

WORLD ENERGY CONSUMPTION—1966
(in thousands of kilowatt hours)

NORTH AMERICA
EUROPE
U.S.S.R.
ASIA
CENTRAL SOUTH AMERICA
AFRICA
OCEANIA
MIDDLE EAST

0   200 400 600 800 1,000 1,200 1,400

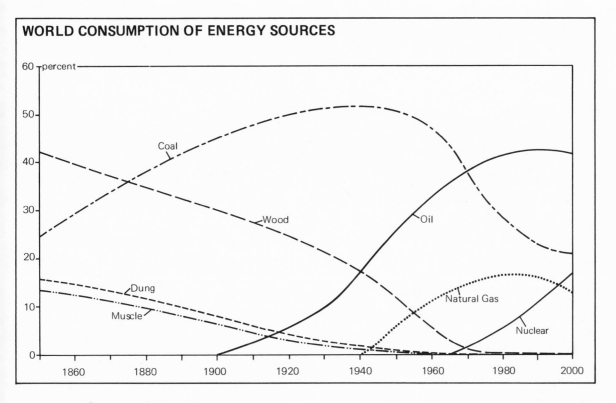

WORLD CONSUMPTION OF ENERGY SOURCES

—is our production capability within reasonable sight of demand.[71]

We can expect the world's total yearly production of crude oil to reach a peak sometime around the turn of the century, with the "middle 80 percent" of this resource likely to be exhausted in under seven decades. The consumption of coal will be more attenuated, however, reaching a peak in 130 to 200 years.[72]

During the 11-year period 1955-66 the average annual rate of growth of electrical energy production was a slightly lower 6.4 percent. At this rate of increase, electrical energy production doubles in just under 11 years; and if even this lower rate of growth were to be sustained for the next 30 years, American society would be consuming 11.0 trillion kilowatt

hours of electricity annually at the turn of the century.[73]

One of the few analyses of industrial use of electricity available is that in a 1963 publication, "Resources for America's Future." It shows the primary metals industry as by far the largest present consumer of electricity. Much of this, in turn, is accounted for by aluminum production, which consumes about ten percent of all industrial power use. The two million tons of aluminum produced in 1960 accounted for more that 38 billion kilowatt hours during the year.[74]

Automobile manufacturing, which purchased 1.5 billion kilowatt hours in 1962, is also a significant consumer of electric power. The rapid growth of this industry is, in part, predicated by the high

MAN AFFAIRS IN TIME PERSPECTIVE

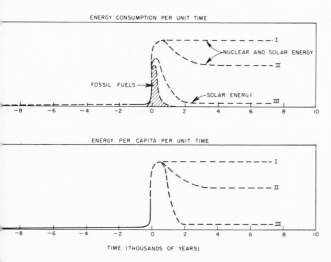

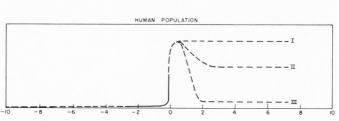

"The present state of human affairs can perhaps more clearly be seen in terms of a time perspective, minus and plus, of some thousands of years with respect to the present, as depicted ... On such a scale the phenomena of present interest -- the growth in the rate of consumption of energy, the growth of the human population, and the rise in the standard of living as indicated by the increase in the per capita rate in energy consumption -- are all seen to be represented by curves which are near zero and rising almost imperceptibly until the last few centuries. Then after an initial gradual increase, each curve, as the present is approached, rises almost vertically to magnitudes many times greater than ever before.

On this time scale the consumption of fossil fuels is seen to rise sharply from zero and almost as sharply to descend, with the total duration of the period of consumption representing but a brief interval of the total period of human history."

rate of replacement of cars which are discarded in favor of new models. The economic benefits of this kind of expansion must eventually be balanced against its environmental costs.

The largest factor in the increase of electric power consumption projected for residential and commercial uses is the appearance of electric heating in homes and business establishments. The goal of the untility industry reported in the Federal Power Commission Survey is 19 million electrically heated homes by 1980. The Resources for the Future's high estimate for 1980 is 18 million electrically heated homes, which would require 166 billion kilowatt hours. This alone is almost equal to the entire residential use of electricity in 1960.[75]

Much of the rise in energy consumption, however, can be accounted for by increases in the high-energy economies; e.g., the United States consumed about one-third of the world's total industrial energy and has less than seven percent of the world's population; Europe and the U.S.S.R. showed corresponding increases.

Our past and present uses of industrial energies, and the prospects forward from such continued fuel uses underline the critical nature of world energy availability both for the developed as well as the underdeveloped regions.

The industrial regions dominate the consumption of each of the industrial fuels . . . consumed 77 percent of the world's most important energy source, coal, in 1963; 81 percent of the world's petroleum; 95 percent of all natural gas; and 80 percent of hydroelectricity and nuclear power . . . the non-industrial world with 71 percent of the world's population used 77 percent of all human energy; 87 percent of all animal energy and 73 percent of total fuel wood and waste in 1963.[76]

In round terms, the total energy supply in 1964 was an average of 1.6 short tons (coal equivalent) for each person in the world. The increase in the high-energy economies further dramatizes the gap between these and those of the low-energy, developing regions: in per capita terms, the more fortunate individuals in the former consumed more than fifty times the industrial energy of their counterparts in the poorer regions.

Power is now the key to expanding food production, the most immediately pressing problem in the highly populated, less-developed regions. Their need is not merely the stop-gap aid of food surpluses or fertilizer shipments, but energy for transport, communications, and distribution facilities, and for local fertilizer production, industralization, and education.

The emergent countries with their dense populations living in small towns and villages need energy badly for light, for village industries, for the irrigation of crops and drainage and for the local processing of their harvest of sugar, cotton, and jute. Energy for transport is also essential for their development. The solution of their energy problems should, therefore, be one of the first objectives of

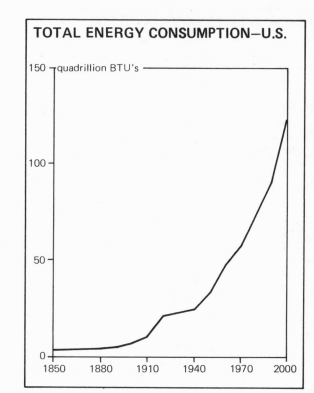

TOTAL ENERGY CONSUMPTION—U.S.

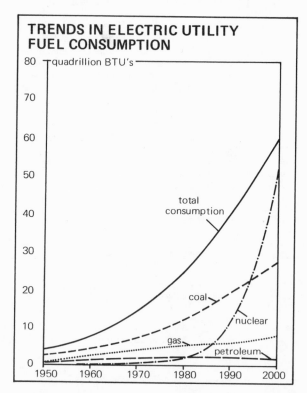

TRENDS IN ELECTRIC UTILITY FUEL CONSUMPTION

technical aid, if the gap between the developed and emergent countries is to be reduced.[77]

Though the rate of industrialization is slow in the developing regions, some already show a growth rate of electricity consumption of 15 to 22 percent. It is calculated, therefore, that just to maintain double our present world population in the next

30 years with no attempt to raise standards of living will require not double but over five times our current rate of energy production.

It should be soberly realized that to bring the lesser developed regions up to industrial parity by building their industries on the same pattern of fuel use and materials consumption as the advanced regions is probably not possible in present terms, i.e., in terms of our currently wasteful practices, misuse of energies, and low performance per unit of energy invested.

In addition to the vast increase in energies required, our present supply of major metals would not suffice. For example, if we were to consider seriously the extension of full-scale electrification to the lesser developed regions, in terms of current technology in practice, we may note that the average use of copper in the industrialized nations is approximately 120 pounds per capita. With such extended electrification the increase of even one pound per capita consumption would require 36 percent increase in world copper production. In energy terms the cost would also be considerable as we need to process over six times as much ore today to obtain the same amount of copper as in 1900. Projecting forward it has been estimated that:

> If the whole world were to reach our current kilowatt hour level at a time when the human population is 5 billion, it would necessitate a ninefold increase in the generation of electricity.[78]

Even in the advanced countries, now facing cuts, seasonal shortages and "brown outs" for the first time in their recent high-energy cycle, power generation and supply has become a critical issue.

Our present problems, even as our future requirements, call for the swiftest increase in the development and utilization of power sources which lessen dependence on fossil fuels. This may be particularly applicable to the lesser developed regions which are lowest in these resources but correspondingly high in access to solar, hydro, and tidal power sources. We need more rigorous investment and development in:

1. alternative means of high energy conversion.
2. the extension of ultra-high voltage transmission networks to obviate the duplication and energy losses in conventional generation and transmission means.
3. more locally autonomous power and "storage" sources—from solar, wind, and hydropower to fuel cell and other "unconventional" sources for local agri-industrial usage, communications, transport, and other needs.
4. the more efficient and continual redesign of our environment tools, facilities, etc., and their "prime-mover" energy converters—toward extraction of maximum performance per unit of energy invested.

This latter set of requirements may be the more pressing even in the advanced countries where there is no energy policy regulating the manufacture and systemic use of domestic energy appliances, energy economy standards of industrial performance, etc.

Energy conversion efficiency is a crucial aspect of the overall energy picture. Present world efficiency is suggested as attaining only about six to eight percent—at best up to 20 percent [79] when we deduct friction, heat, engine wear, malfunction, poor fuel oxidation, losses in transmission, overloading, inefficient use due to poorly designed buildings, etc.

Fossil fuel steam-generating plants convert only 30 to 35 percent of the total thermal energy into electricity. The remaining 65 to 70 percent must be dissipated, usually in a body of water. Nuclear plants are considerably less efficient and are unlikely to match the efficiency of fossil fuel plants within the next 20 years.

Looking then to the year 2000, one discovers that the waste heat that would result from the production of 11.0 trillion kilowatt hours of electrical energy would be sufficient to raise the temperature of the total annual freshwater runoff from the conterminous United States by 24 degrees F. Quite clearly, even if 11.0 trillion kilowatt hours were to be produced in the year 2000, only a fraction of this power could be generated at inland sites.

The automobile is a particularly good example of inefficiency: of the energy in crude oil, 13 percent is lost in refining; 3 percent is used in transport to the consumer; 25 percent is converted to work in the engine, but only 30 percent of this amount is transmitted to the road (after losses due to friction and auto auxiliaries); and further decreases occur through gears and tires. The overall efficiency of the automobile is about five percent, although air drag, braking, and idling reduce this even further in actual operation.

Few detailed energy budget analyses have been applied to urban and other systems in terms of their energy efficiency. Present attention to the malfunction of the automobile in cities could be usefully extended to lighting, heating, cooling, sewage, and waste disposal systems.

A great deal may, therefore, be accomplished merely by increasing our overall energy conversion efficiency. More rigorous design of present use systems is needed and more attention to their duplicative use of separately functioning appliances, etc., which use different power/fuel sources, for related end purposes. Doubling and tripling of performance per energy unit invested would be possible.

In overall terms, for example, we have no guide estimates of how much energy we presently expend to procure and use energy, i.e., computed from the extractive and industrial base outwardly to its myriad end uses.

ENERGY CONVERSION EFFICIENCIES

A. PROGRESS IN EFFICIENCY OF STEAM-ENGINES

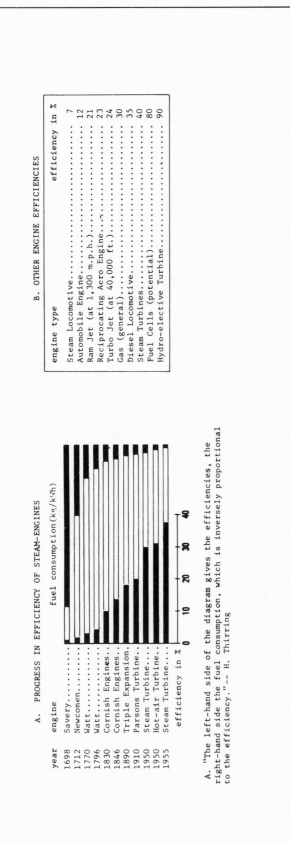

A. "The left-hand side of the diagram gives the efficiencies, the right-hand side the fuel consumption, which is inversely proportional to the efficiency." -- H. Thirring

B. OTHER ENGINE EFFICIENCIES

engine type	efficiency in %
Steam Locomotive	7
Automobile Engine	12
Ram Jet (at 1,300 m.p.h.)	21
Reciprocating Aero Engine	23
Turbo Jet (at 40,000 ft.)	24
Gas (general)	30
Diesel Locomotive	35
Parsons Turbine	40
Steam Turbines	80
Fuel Cells (potential)	80
Hydro-electric Turbine	90

OVERALL EFFICIENCIES OF STEAM ELECTRIC PLANTS

Fossil fueled plant*	38 to 40%
Proposed fossil fueled plants with MHD topping cycle**	53 to 59%
Present light water nuclear reactor plants***	30 to 32%
Proposed advanced nuclear reator plants	39 to 43%

*Approximately 15—20 percent of the waste heat from a fossil fueled plant is discharged via the stack and the remainder is discharged via the condenser to the cooling water stream.

**MHD stands for a new method of producing electricity called magnetohydrodynamics.

***Essentially all of the waste heat from a nuclear plant is discharged via the condenser to the cooling water stream.

EFFICIENCY OF ENERGY CONVERSION SYSTEMS

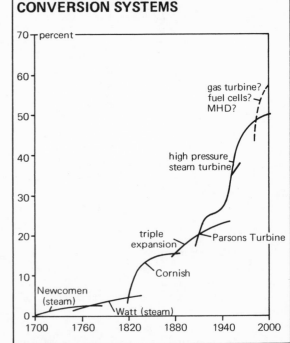

MATERIALS. The processes of metals and minerals extraction, distribution, use, and circulation in our industrial systems are now a major subsystem of the biosphere. Our large-scale industrial networks are now operable as externalized metabolic systems. We might more fruitfully examine the progressive extractions, flows, and recyclings of

RELATIVE ABUNDANCE OF ELEMENTS IN THE SEA

	TONS PER CU. MILE		TONS PER CU. MILE		TONS PER CU. MILE
CHLORINE	89,500,000	INDIUM	94	SILVER	1
SODIUM	49,500,000	ZINC	47	LANTHANUM	1
MAGNESIUM	6,400,000	IRON	47	KRYPTON	1
SULFUR	4,200,000	ALUMINIUM	47	NEON	0.5
CALCIUM	1,900,000	MOLYBDENUM	47	CADMIUM	0.5
POTASSIUM	1,800,000	SELENIUM	19	TUNGSTEN	0.5
BROMINE	306,000	TIN	14	XENON	0.5
CARBON	132,000	COPPER	14	GERMANIUM	0.3
STRONTIUM	38,000	ARSENIC	14	CHROMIUM	0.2
BORON	23,000	URANIUM	14	THORIUM	0.2
SILICON	14,000	NICKEL	9	SCANDIUM	0.2
FLUORINE	6,100	VANADIUM	9	LEAD	0.1
ARGON	2,800	MANGANESE	9	MERCURY	0.1
NITROGEN	2,400	TITANIUM	5	GALLIUM	0.1
LITHIUM	800	ANTIMONY	2	BISMUTH	0.1
RUBIDIUM	570	COBALT	2	NIOBIUM	0.05
PHOSPHORUS	330	CESIUM	2	THALLIUM	0.05
IODINE	280	CERIUM	2	HELIUM	0.03
BARIUM	140	YTTRIUM	1	GOLD	0.02

RELATIVE ABUNDANCE OF ELEMENTS IN THE EARTH

	P.P.M.		P.P.M.		P.P.M.
SILICON	277,200	COLUMBIUM	24	HOLMIUM	1.2
ALUMINUM	81,300	NEODYMIUM	24	EUROPIUM	1.1
IRON	50,000	COBALT	23	ANTIMONY	1
CALCIUM	36,300	LANTHANIUM	18	TERBIUM	0.9
SODIUM	28,300	LEAD	16	LUTETIUM	0.8
POTASSIUM	25,900	GALLIUM	15	THALLIUM	0.6
MAGNESIUM	20,900	MOLYBDENUM	15	MERCURY	0.5
TITANIUM	4,400	THORIUM	12	BISMUTH	0.2
MANGANESE	1,000	CESIUM	7	THULIUM	0.2
RUBIDIUM	310	GERMANIUM	7	CADMIUM	0.15
STRONTIUM	300	SAMARIUM	6.5	INDIUM	0.1
BARIUM	250	GADOLINIUM	6.4	SILVER	0.1
ZIRCONIUM	220	BERYLLIUM	6	SELENIUM	0.09
CHROMIUM	200	PRAESODYMIUM	5.5	PALLADIUM	0.01
VANADIUM	150	ARSENIC	5	GOLD	0.005
ZINC	132	SCANDIUM	5	PLATINUM	0.005
NICKEL	80	DYSPROSIUM	4.5	TELLURIUM	0.002
COPPER	70	HAFNIUM	4.5	IRIDIUM	0.001
TUNGSTEN	69	URANIUM	4	OSMIUM	0.001
LITHIUM	65	BORON	3	RHENIUM	0.001
CERIUM	46	YTTERBIUM	2.7	RHODIUM	0.001
TIN	40	ERBIUM	2.5	RUTHENIUM	0.001
YTTRIUM	28	TANTALUM	2.1		

their materials in terms of overall metabolic, or ecological efficiency rather than through their customary analysis in economic, fiscal, and trade exchange terms.

Our present modes of conceptualizing material usage in our industrial ecology relate more to the preindustrial past than to the realities of a critically interdependent global network. Restrictive trade, barter, and accounting procedures which flow from this lag in conception may be as dangerous to our forward maintenance as glandular malfunction in the internal human metabolism.

We may note, in passing, that many of the industrial resources presently in use were not even conceptually recognized as such a little over a century ago. Aluminum was a scarce metallic curiosity, radioactivity a laboratory phenomenon, and many of our present key metals were regarded as waste impurities in other ores. The capacities of our material resources depend on the way we view our environment—they are, ultimately, as we perceive them to be.

We refer to industrial raw materials as those generally found in the earth crust—a ten-mile-thick shell of geological formed deposits used in our present technologies.

In addition to these crust materials are the elements of the atmosphere and ocean that are used in the industrial process. Eight elements make up 98.6 percent of the earth crust.

WORLD PRODUCTION OF MAJOR MINERALS AND METALS BY COUNTRY 1968

MINERALS	WORLD PRODUCTION	LEADING COUNTRY	PRODUCTION
ALUMINUM	8,285,415 S.T.	UNITED STATES	3,269,259
ANTIMONY	64,402 S.T.	SOUTH AFRICA	14,216
ASBESTOS	3,359,006 S.T. (1966)	CANADA	1,479,281
BAUXITE	43,612,000 L.T.	JAMAICA	9,121,000
CEMENT (all hydraulic)	2,813,855,000 B.B.L.	U.S.S.R.	497,208,000
CHROMIUM	5,110,833 S.T.	U.S.S.R.	1,731,000
COAL (all grades)	3,002,581,000 S.T.	U.S.S.R.	656,000,000
COBALT	20,045 S.T.	CONGO (Kinshasa)	10,709
COPPER (mined)	5,435,787 S.T.	UNITED STATES	954,064
FLUORSPAR	3,150,488 S.T.	MEXICO	785,114
GOLD	45,610,000 T.O.	SOUTH AFRICA	30,532,880
GYPSUM	49,629,000 S.T.	UNITED STATES	9,647,000
IRON ORE	618,308,000 L.T.	U.S.S.R.	165,347
LEAD (mined)	3,132,887 S.T.	U.S.S.R.	440,000
MAGNESIUM	202,608 S.T.	UNITED STATES	97,406
MANGANESE	18,650,000 S.T.	U.S.S.R.	7,940,000
MERCURY	245,042 F.	SPAIN	50,000
MICA	319,943,000 LBS. (1966)	UNITED STATES	226,267,000
MOLYBDENUM	125,363,000 LBS.	UNITED STATES	88,930,000
NATURAL GAS	28,384,031 Mil. Cu. Ft.	UNITED STATES	18,171,325
NICKEL	481,269 S.T.	CANADA	246,954
PETROLEUM	12,889,705,000 B.B.L.	UNITED STATES	3,215,742,000
PHOSPHATE ROCK	86,969,000 S.T.	UNITED STATES	39,770,000
PLATINUM GROUP	3,154,434 T.O.	U.S.S.R.	1,900,000
POTASH	16,861,197 S.T.	UNITED STATES	3,299,000
SALT	111,304,000 S.T.	UNITED STATES	38,958,000
SILVER	260,820,000 T.O.	MEXICO	37,939,498
STEEL	543,080,000 S.T.	UNITED STATES	127,213,000
SULFUR	17,247,167 L.T.	CANADA	2,073,413
TIN (mined)	211,664 L.T.	MALAYSIA	72,121
TITANIUM (ILMENITE)	2,959,965 S.T.	UNITED STATES	935,091
TUNGSTEN	38,690,000 LBS.	UNITED STATES	13,860,000
URANIUM (non-Communist)	17,058 S.T.	UNITED STATES	9,125
VANADIUM	10,595 S.T.	UNITED STATES	4,963
ZINC (mined)	5,175,463 S.T.	CANADA	1,248,977

S.T.	Short ton	T.O.	Troy ounce
L.T.	Long ton	F.	Flask
B.B.L.	Barrel		

The major concentrations of these resources are inequably distributed around the earth and have been an important factor in the location of industries, growth of living standards, and the present disparities between rich and poor nations.

The industrial revolutions of the nineteenth century began the production of metals on an abruptly larger scale than any previous period. In the first quarter of the twentieth century more metal of every type was extracted and processed than in the whole of all recorded history; this output was doubled in the second quarter of the century. Ninety percent of this production was iron-alloyed with a smaller proportion of other metals to form the range of steels which have been the fundamental materials basis for our present industrial civilization.

There are three phases of industrial growth and materials usage which are important:

1. The first phase was marked by the localized growth of iron and steel production when large-scale mechanical industry developed in those countries where supplies of iron ore, coal, etc., were available close to power sources. The swift "take-off" of the industrially advanced countries owes much to these locally convenient factors.
2. The second phase occurs in the late nineteenth and early twentieth century when new steels and other alloy production required access to a greater range of resources which were relatively scarce in the then industrial countries, i.e., manganese, tungsten, nickel, cobalt, etc., were unevenly dispersed around the globe. This phase was marked by intense competition for control of these resources particularly in the underdeveloped countries. The key concentration of industrial power was in steel production paired with heavy dependence on coal and oil fuels as the major energy resource.
3. The third phase, which we are just entering, is characterized by the increasing displacement of steel as the prime industrial material (for structural, machine, transport, and other uses) by other light metals, composite materials, and plastics. The forward pattern of industrial development lies (1) in the pairing of the light metals with electrical power from hydro or nuclear sources (2) in the increased use of metallics and nonmetallic composites and plastics with similar power sources. These developments could swiftly alter the present industrial power balance and, importantly, could eventually turn the present "prior investment" advantage of the older established industrial regions into a restrictive disability.

Our present emphasis on metals is based, therefore, on the continuing centrality of their position within the industrial ecology and, even more importantly, on the critical aspects of overall metal

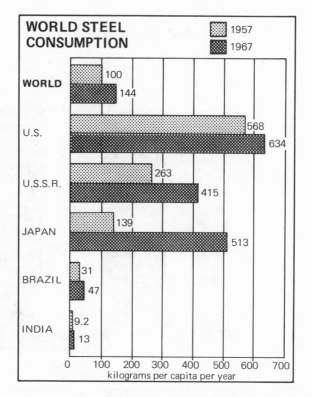

WORLD STEEL CONSUMPTION

1957
1967

WORLD 100 / 144
U.S. 568 / 634
U.S.S.R. 263 / 415
JAPAN 139 / 513
BRAZIL 31 / 47
INDIA 9.2 / 13

kilograms per capita per year

resources in our current transitional period. Until other materials are more fully developed and available in the same abundance with the necessary ranges of tensile stress, hardness, durability, energy conductance, forming capacities, and so forth, we are heavily dependent upon the key metals.

The high living standards afforded by advanced technological facilities are predicated largely on the amounts of metals and inanimate energies available. As the amount of metal used in maintaining such living standards increases in overall consumption with the numbers of persons served by an increasing range of industrial facilities, the amount of metals actually available per capita decreases.

Within the immediate range of our present technologies we are dealing with a relatively limited amount of metal resources. Alloy chemistry may extend the number of their combinations and provides an increasing range of qualities; the reuse of the metals and their alloys through progressive cycles of scrapping and refabrication in different products means that they are not "lost" or used up.

In the long run, when we consider such factors, metals are inexhaustible. But, if we wish to increase our immediate advantage industrially—to serve more men with higher living standards—we must do this in the shortest possible time by extracting more designed performance from each unit of metal used.

The gain of higher performance per materials used investment is a "natural" aspect of advance technological development. Each successive technical improvement is designed to reduce materials and energy "costs" per function. This is dramatically evident in the progressive miniaturization of many

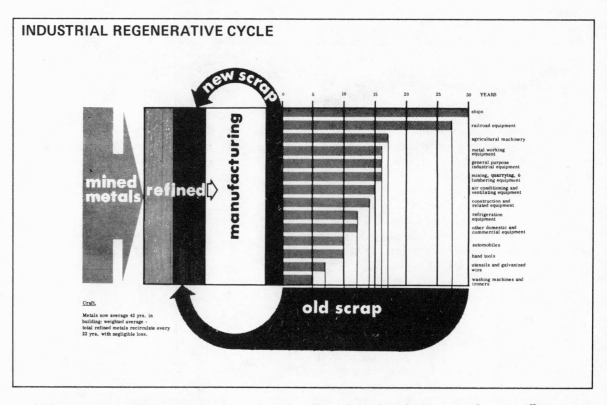

INDUSTRIAL REGENERATIVE CYCLE

new scrap

0   5   10   15   20   25   30   YEARS

mined metals refined

manufacturing

ships
railroad equipment
agricultural machinery
metal working equipment
general purpose industrial equipment
mining, quarrying, & lumbering equipment
air conditioning and ventilating equipment
construction and related equipment
refrigeration equipment
other domestic and commercial equipment
automobiles
hand tools
utensils and galvanized wire
washing machines and ironers

old scrap

Craft.

Metals now average 42 yrs. in building: weighted average - total refined metals recirculate every 22 yrs, with negligible loss.

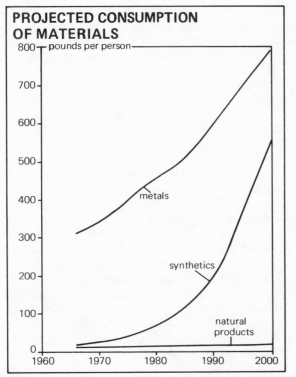

PROJECTED CONSUMPTION OF MATERIALS

800 pounds per person

700

600

500

400 metals

300

200 synthetics

100

0 natural products

1960 1970 1980 1990 2000

fore, through redesign toward more efficient performance in the use-cycle of our major materials. Though inherent within technological development, the swift increase in the overall amounts of materials used, in the range of industrial facilities, and the number of users, requires that we more consciously redirect and hasten this process—or we may be overtaken by the inevitable conflicts which our present "have/have not" disparities engender.

The rate at which the "invasion" of traditional metal areas by new materials takes place is not simply gauged by "functional" replacement, but is determined more by the degree of investment in older materials, established plant production procedures, and many other factors.

The more swiftly moving determinants of forward resource-use patterns now are not the established industries tied into steel, but advanced transportation, communications, etc. Their use of materials is, comparatively, of less bulk weight and they extract much higher performance per unit of material and energy investment—factors which are not so apparent in classical economics and trade analyses.

As we come down through the uses of plastics in various industrial sectors, we might almost gauge the level of technological advance in each by its use of materials, e.g., aerospace, aircraft, and automobiles. Though marine technology is one of the oldest sectors, its irruption into "below surface" areas has given it a new technological dimension as rigorous in its performance demands as aerospace. One of the least advanced technological sectors is in building construction, which typically uses less structural plastic than other major areas. Its overall bulk uses

devices and by the reduction of material weight, prime mover, and maintenance energies in advanced technologies of transportation, communication, and information handling (see chart on computer performance gains).

Extending advanced living standards to more people despite decreasing amounts of available metals and other materials per capita is only feasible, there-

POPULATION / MATERIALS: PROJECTED CONSUMPTION

	YEAR	1966	1970	1980	1985	1990	2000
	POPULATION (billions)	3.4	3.7	4.6	5.0	5.6	7.0
METALS	IRON						
	Mil. tons	469.0	560.0	900.0	1130.0	1400.0	2250.0
	Lbs./person	304.0	332.0	431.0	497.0	550.0	706.0
	ALUMINUM						
	Mil. tons	7.7	11.3	32.0	55.0	90.0	250.0
	Lbs./person	5.0	7.0	15.0	24.0	35.0	79.0
	COPPER						
	Mil. tons	5.4	6.2	9.2	10.0	13.5	20.0
	Lbs./person	4.0	4.0	4.0	4.0	5.0	6.0
	ZINC						
	Mil. tons	4.3	5.0	7.2	8.7	10.4	15.0
	Lbs./person	3.0	3.0	4.0	4.0	4.0	4.0
	TOTAL METALS						
	Mil. tons	486.0	582.0	948.0	1204.0	1514.0	2535.0
	Lbs./person	315.0	345.0	453.0	503.0	594.0	795.0
	Mil. cu. m.	64.0	78.0	129.0	167.0	215.0	384.0
	Liters/person	19.0	21.0	28.0	33.0	38.0	55.0
SYNTHETICS	PLASTICS						
	Mil. tons	16.0	27.0	105.0	240.0	420.0	1700.0
	Lbs./person	10.0	16.0	50.0	116.0	165.0	535.0
	SYNTHETIC RUBBERS						
	Mil. tons	3.9	5.5	11.5	16.0	23.0	44.0
	Lbs./person	2.0	3.0	6.0	7.0	9.0	14.0
	MAN-MADE FIBERS						
	Mil. tons	5.6	7.2	13.0	17.0	24.5	46.0
	Lbs./person	4.0	4.0	6.0	7.0	10.0	15.0
	TOTAL SYNTHETICS						
	Mil. tons	25.5	40.0	130.0	273.0	467.0	1790.0
	Lbs./person	17.0	24.0	62.0	121.0	183.0	563.0
	Mil. cu. m.	23.0	35.0	114.0	236.0	409.0	1564.0
	Liters/person	6.8	9.5	25.0	47.0	73.0	224.0
NATURAL PRODUCTS	NATURAL RUBBER						
	Mil. tons	2.2	2.5	2.6	2.7	2.8	3.0
	Lbs./person	1.0	2.0	1.0	1.0	1.0	1.0
	NATURAL FIBERS						
	Mil. tons	19.0	21.5	30.2	35.0	41.5	60.0
	Lbs./person	12.0	13.0	15.0	15.0	16.0	19.0
	TOTAL NATURAL PROD.						
	Mil. tons	21.2	24.0	32.8	37.7	44.3	63.0
	Lbs./person	14.0	14.0	16.0	17.0	17.0	20.0
	Mil. cu. m.	18.4	20.7	27.7	31.9	37.5	53.2
	Liters/person	5.4	5.6	6.0	6.4	6.7	7.6
TOTALS	Million tons	533.0	646.0	1111.0	1515.0	2025.0	4388.0
	Lbs./person	345.0	385.0	530.0	667.0	794.0	1379.0
	Mil. cu. m.	105.0	134.0	271.0	435.0	662.0	2001.0
	Liters/person	31.0	36.0	59.0	87.0	118.0	286.0

of plastics represent other functions such as internal surfacing, appliances, etc.

Plastics are beginning to take over from the steels and other common metal alloys in increasing proportions. The pattern is partially obscured by the difference in weight/volume measures obtaining in the two areas of metals and plastics. One weight unit of plastic may replace the same weight unit of metal, but the volume displacement may be much greater due to their difference in density. Analysis of cost comparisons of metals to plastic is already conducted in volumetric terms, e.g., plastics are now cheaper than steel, aluminum, or magnesium for various uses on a cost per cubic inch basis.

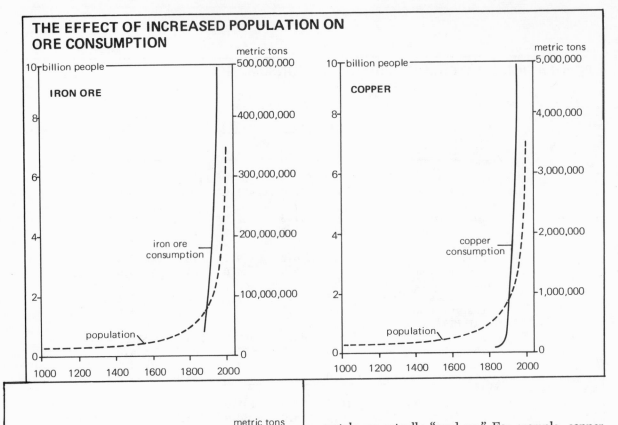

THE EFFECT OF INCREASED POPULATION ON ORE CONSUMPTION

metals are actually "used up." For example, copper production in the United States now uses 42 percent of recovered industrial scrap annually and this percentage rises as the importance of closing the scrap/reuse cycle becomes more evident and economical.

As we have noted, most of them are highly recoverable through their scrapping cycles and are, therefore, used over and over again. Our "reserves," therefore, include all metals in present use and those recoverable from the lowest-grade ore deposits in the earth's crust, which are not usually accounted for in terms of "exploitability"—as not being economically exploitable in present terms.

By 1985 oil and natural gas will have become the source of about 90 percent of all organic chemicals. Nevertheless, these are produced from only a small percentage of the total amount of petroleum which is extracted from the earth. Indeed, the country's (Great Britain's) chemical industry today uses only about 2½ percent of all the petroleum produced; by 1985, it is expected to be about 5 percent, and by 2000 perhaps 12 percent.[80]

METAL RESERVES AND FUTURE USES. Most analyses of world resource materials deal in "years of supply in exploitable reserves." For example:

Aluminum	570 years	Copper	29 years
Iron	250 years	Lead	19 years
Zinc	23 years	Tin	35 years

Such estimates are useful for general economic criteria. However, their use is limited by their lack of appreciation of the limited degree to which such

Of course, present availability is important in the next critical transition in access to industrial parity for the poorer nations. In dealing with energy resource reserves, the key question is how we may bring the underdeveloped nations up to better standards of living, that is, as measured by present materially advanced regions. It has been noted, for example, "that the U.S. with only six percent of the world's population, consumes approximately 30 percent of the world's total current production of minerals."

MATERIALS REPLACED BY PLASTICS
estimated replacement of selected materials by plastics in 1970

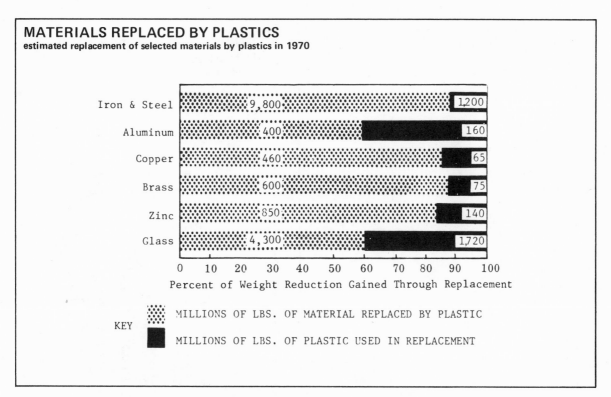

Iron & Steel	9,800 / 1,200
Aluminum	400 / 160
Copper	460 / 65
Brass	600 / 75
Zinc	850 / 140
Glass	4,300 / 1,720

Percent of Weight Reduction Gained Through Replacement

KEY
MILLIONS OF LBS. OF MATERIAL REPLACED BY PLASTIC
MILLIONS OF LBS. OF PLASTIC USED IN REPLACEMENT

LIFETIMES OF WORLD METAL RESERVES

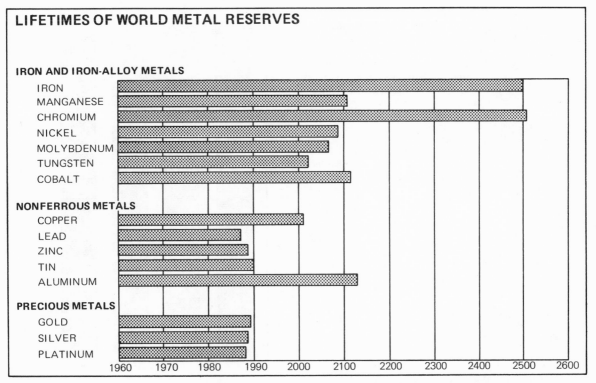

IRON AND IRON-ALLOY METALS
IRON
MANGANESE
CHROMIUM
NICKEL
MOLYBDENUM
TUNGSTEN
COBALT

NONFERROUS METALS
COPPER
LEAD
ZINC
TIN
ALUMINUM

PRECIOUS METALS
GOLD
SILVER
PLATINUM

1960 1970 1980 1990 2000 2100 2200 2300 2400 2500 2600

World demand for twenty key minerals is expected to double by 1988 and triple by the year 2000 . . . the U.S. is almost totally dependent on foreign sources for . . . chromium, manganese, nickel, cobalt, tin, and industrial diamonds . . . domestic sources are a small factor in the supply of such important minerals as aluminum, zinc, and tungsten.[81]

Each year, for every person in our country, over 3.5 tons of stone, sand, and gravel must be dug from the earth, transported, and used in one way or another. Each of us uses, directly or indirectly, every year, over 500 pounds of cement, nearly 400 pounds of clay, over 200 pounds of common salt, and over 100 pounds of phosphate rock. Altogether, over 20 tons of raw materials must be dug from the earth and processed each year in order to support a single individual in our society.[82]

The Department of the Interior estimates that the value of the projected demand for primary minerals in the year 2000 will total more than $60 billion—a fourfold increase over the present schedule. Specifically, demands for aluminum and titanium are expected to increase sixfold; for tungsten and vana-

FOREIGN METALS IN A U.S. AUTO

	TOTAL POUNDS	FROM FOREIGN COUNTRIES
IRON	3,705	36%
COPPER	52	38%
LEAD	24	58%
ALUMINUM	48	89%
ZINC	123	59%
OTHER MATERIALS	415	—

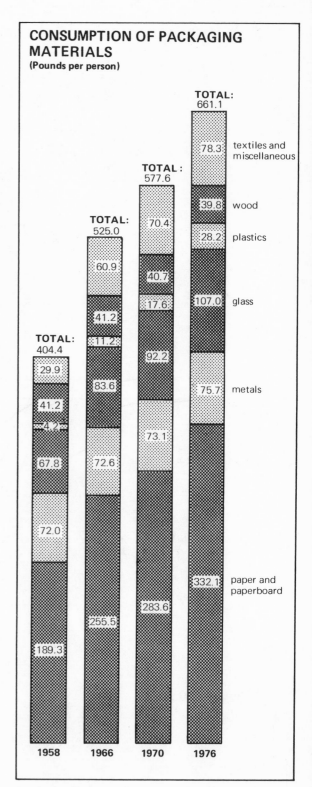

CONSUMPTION OF PACKAGING MATERIALS
(Pounds per person)

dium, fourfold; for copper, sand, and gravel, crushed stone, beryllium, fluorine, tantalum, and magnesium, a threefold increase, and for a host of other commodities a twofold increase.

What does this mean in real numbers—between now and then? It means more than seven billion tons of iron ore, more than one billion tons of aluminum ore; more than one billion tons of phosphate rock; more than 100 million tons of copper, etc.

By the year 2000 we expect also that water usage will triple: that total energy requirements will triple; and that we will have to construct again as many houses and other facilities as now exist in the United States. This staggering demand for hard mineral resources imposes a gigantic task of new discovery and new development, not only in the United States but throughout the world.[83]

. . . the United States accounts for 38 percent of the world's yearly pulp consumption. With Canada and Europe it accounts for over 80 percent, though these three areas combined have only 20 percent of the world's population.[84]

60 percent of all the rubber and 21 percent of all the steel consumed in the U.S. go into the manufacture of motor vehicles.[85]

We might then ask how much more would be required to bring the total world population up to the same level of material consumption? This comes out to about five times the present world production of minerals—far more than we can attain with present levels of materials and energy performance efficiencies.

Using an ordinary example, suppose we tried to extend the 1960 level of U.S. automobile use (at roughly one auto per three people) to the entire world population. This would require approximately 2,300 million tons of steel—as against total world

steel production (1963) of only 425 million tons. Such a statement is, of course, in part ridiculous since the industrial-based system required to sustain such an extended production and use of automobiles (as presently designed and used) at this world scale, would require not only the amount of metals and full energies, etc., for the autos but for all the myriad other subsystems which this one item con-

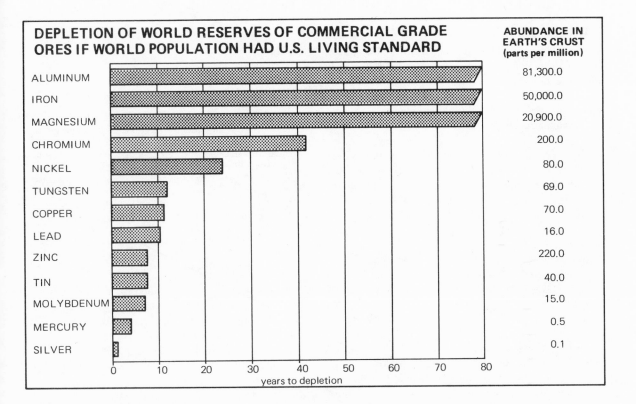

DEPLETION OF WORLD RESERVES OF COMMERCIAL GRADE ORES IF WORLD POPULATION HAD U.S. LIVING STANDARD

ABUNDANCE IN EARTH'S CRUST (parts per million)

Ore	Abundance
ALUMINUM	81,300.0
IRON	50,000.0
MAGNESIUM	20,900.0
CHROMIUM	200.0
NICKEL	80.0
TUNGSTEN	69.0
COPPER	70.0
LEAD	16.0
ZINC	220.0
TIN	40.0
MOLYBDENUM	15.0
MERCURY	0.5
SILVER	0.1

years to depletion

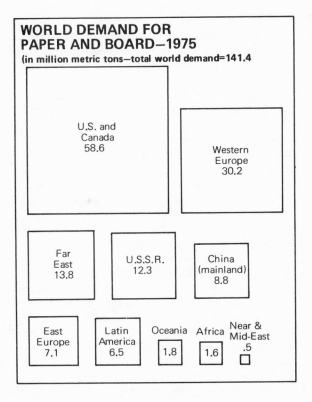

WORLD DEMAND FOR PAPER AND BOARD—1975

(in million metric tons—total world demand=141.4)

U.S. and Canada 58.6

Western Europe 30.2

Far East 13.8

U.S.S.R. 12.3

China (mainland) 8.8

East Europe 7.1

Latin America 6.5

Oceania 1.8

Africa 1.6

Near & Mid-East .5

ments in this text, is to ask what may be the maximal carrying capacity for the biosphere in terms of human population, and what energies and resources are required to sustain such a population at reasonable living standards. Current quantitatively biased growth projections and associated trends obtaining in the industrialized nations already show that this carrying capacity may be easily overtaxed as more and more materials are used and more heat energies and pollutants are dissipated in their consumption and redistribution.

Many of our currently prodigal modes of using the earth and biosphere systems are potentially more dangerous every year. We dissipate vast quantities of capital energies which we may need in future emergencies, and we disperse vast concentrations of materials that we have no present means of reconstituting. This extends to our use of soils, air, and water, and to our complex interdependence on other life forms.

Even when we say, for example, that metals and other materials may be inexhaustible in terms of recycling and reuse, this is a relative statement only—that is, relative to the necessarily massive reorganization of our priorities and goals which may enable us to plan a more closed-loop-type of human ecology.

siperation entails. No mere duplication of present standards will suffice to close the gap.

SOME END QUESTIONS. It is obvious that in addition to exercising more economy in the use of metals and other materials, we will have to temper our assessment of possible growth patterns both in the advanced and lesser developed regions. The end question, returning to the early part of our com-

The percentage of (paper) production that is recycled is historically about 20 percent. If, in addition, the annual recycle can be increased by 50 percent of the projected growth, or 25 million net tons by 1985, the saving would be equivalent to 31 million cords of wood—more than two and one-half times the present total annual production of the four leading states—Georgia, Washington, Alabama, and Florida.[86]

The planning of that qualitatively balanced human ecology must be considered in global terms. Some of the mandatory requirements for the merely adequate maintenance of the ecosystem are already clear. We need to redesign our major social, industrial, and agricultural undertakings for more efficient and systematic functioning.

1. to recycle the metals and materials in the system so that there is a swifter turnover with the least lag in scrapping and processing cycles. In high-grade technological process, each use-cycle tends, through overall development, to achieve more, not less, performance per invested unit of materials.
2. to employ increasingly our "income" energies of solar, water, wind, tidal, and nuclear power, rather than the hazardous and depletive fossil fuels. The latter represent major "capital" investments which, once used, are not replaceable. They are too precious to "burn up" in our current prodigal fashion, but they may be more efficiently—and more fractionally—employed in indirect conversion to plastics, foodstuffs, etc.
3. to refashion our food cycle so that we may more swiftly augment the present starvation diets of more than half the developing world. We need, however, to go also beyond emergency satisfaction of immediate needs toward the more extensive ecological redesign of our whole agri-industrial system; employing the most efficient, natural, means of food conversion through the plant/animal chains and the possibilities inherent in microbiological, biosynthetic, and other processes.
4. to set up eco-monitoring and control centers which will act as "early warning systems" in relation to our large-scale scientific and technological undertakings—analyzing and evaluating their immediate and long-range effects on the overall ecological matrix and their positive and negative implications for the quality of the human environ.

The minimal set of basic questions we need to ask ranges far beyond those required for local solutions to our various problems. Many of the problems are only problems because of a parochial concern with an economically or politically "convenient" set of solutions. There are no wholly local solutions any more, just as there are no major human problems that are not also global. The basic questions revolve around the overall ecological maintenance of the entire human community.

What are the optimal conditions for human society on earth? There is obviously no fixed answer to such a question. But there are the various physical factors of adequacy in food, shelter, health, general welfare, and the concomitant access to the individually preferred physical and social facilities that make life meaningful and enjoyable. We have gradually arrived at a set of such conditions, as in the various bills of human rights (e.g., that of the United Nations).

It might bring us to recognize that the lands and their vegetative cover, their resources of minerals and waters, and the seas themselves, are the indispensable commons of the human species as a whole, and that any individual or organizational proprietary rights to any part of them are subordinate to the environmental rights of all people, including at least our immediate heirs. The destruction of forests and the pollution of the oceans for individual or corporate gain may impair our grandchildren's ability to breathe. We may even come to hold that the manufacturer or government bureaucrat responsible for the discharge of poisons into the environment should be as accountable as if he had dumped the crankcase drainings of his motorcar down his neighbor's well or his garbage on his neighbor's porch.[87]

The time is overdue for much more than tentative, local, and piecemeal measures. To find our way forward through our present critical transitions, we need to find some positive and operational indicators of the optimal conditions for the fulfillment of human life. By this, we do not mean optimal determinants that may be valid for all time and all people, that is, a specific set of absolutes. The variable and changing nature of human values makes this not only undesirable but unrealistic, since the development of one set of values may considerably modify others. But such considerations may still be flexibly accommodated and yet allow adequate definition.

We may tackle this in other ways by asking various fundamental questions about our planetary society. Which activities are most inimical to this; which more positively sustain, and forward, the human enterprise? What are the physical limits and constraints in the overall ecosystem with regard to our growing technological systems? What are the irreplaceable resource limits, for example, both the material and physical-energy resources, and the human individual, social, and genetic resources? What are the relevant human biological limits, for example, air, food, water, temperature, space, speed, noise, and density tolerances? What are the essential and desirable psychosocial conditions for full human development, for individual privacy, for freedom of thought and action, for the qualitative and irreducible assessment of human dignity? In many ways, the core of our discussion has revolved around the same inquiry, repeated in different ways: what are the sociophysical operational parameters for the planet—the "housekeeping" rules that govern human occupancy?

These are very large questions, but they are those to which we must now apply ourselves—in many different ways and over a long period. Some of the answers we already know, in part. Others are, in some senses, ultimately unanswerable. But this only gives us more reason to ask them—if only to probe the limits of our knowledge.

COMPARATIVE INDICATORS

URBANISM

In 1900, approximately 10 percent of the world population lived in cities of over a million people. It is estimated that in the period from 1920 to 2000, the urban population in the developing countries will have grown from 100 million to around 2,000 million. Overall, by that time, 38 percent of the world population could be urbanized.

Such estimates assume that trends toward "urban packing" will continue as at present. There are, however, reverse trends in the more developed nations, where the movement from the city's core to suburbia to further deployment is already evident—for those who can afford the mobility.

As with many such trends, they should not be regarded as irreversible—but are more than ever subject to human choice and decision. Generally, in relation to urbanism, our thinking is still oriented to the city as the center of an agricultural society or one in transition through the industrial revolution. Urbanism may be viewed as only one of a number of possible strategies for living in dispersed small groups or larger concentrations, as desired.

We are now in the developing phases of successive "industrial" revolutions in which refined electronic means have displaced most of previous time, energy, and space relationships which were the guidelines of our thinking. The city as the lodestone for earning a higher living may no longer be operative

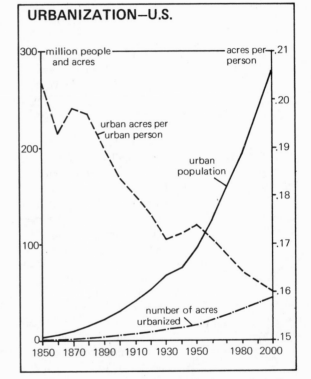

within the concept of automated, dispersed, industrial production plants whose location requires no labor concentrations as did the nineteenth century industrial city.

ESTIMATED ANNUAL HOUSING NEEDS
(in millions of dwelling units)

	AFRICA		ASIA		LATIN AMERICA	
	1960	1975	1960	1975	1960	1975
Due to population increase:	0.84	1.50	5.30	9.40	1.10	1.70
To eliminate the deficit or shortage in 30 years:	.73	.73	4.80	4.80	.60	.60
To replace the stock:*	1.03	1.03	7.10	7.10	.90	.90
Total new housing needed:	2.60	3.26	17.20	21.30	2.60	3.20

* Average life of a dwelling unit is assumed to be 30 years in urban and 20 years in rural areas. The 1975 figures do not take into account increments of stock between 1960 and 1975.

HOUSING

The U.N. estimated in 1961 that about three-fourths of the world's population lived in substandard housing. This would give a figure of roughly 2,400 million people—in terms of six-person family dwelling units, 400 million would be required.

In 1963, a U.S. Senate Committee on International Housing gave the following figures:

It is estimated that over 900 million persons in Africa, Asia, and Latin America are without proper housing . . . if, as is recommended, 30 years were taken as the target to meet the housing shortage, and the average life of a house as approximately 25 years, then annual construction needed for current deficit, necessary for replacement and population growth would be nearly 22 million units. By 1975, required annual construction would be almost 28 million units. The urban areas of Africa, Asia, and Latin America constituting less than 30 percent of the total population would account for over half of the recommended construction.[88]

It has of course, become markedly evident in recent years that much housing in the so-called advanced countries is also inadequate and the housing "industry" is unable to fulfill even long overdue requirements for low, and even middle-income, housing.

EDUCATION

In our developing world civilization, lack of education is a form of disenfranchisement. The illiterate individual is restrained from full participation and access to his birthright as a human being—the right to man's accumulated cultural heritage and to the "practical" augmentation of his living, which may be afforded by access to the highest scientific and technological capability.

We may order the problem of adequate education in various ways, i.e., the need for general education, for scientific and technical skills, training and the

THE EDUCATION GAP

	U.S.	West Europe	U.S.S.R.	Japan	India
% GNP for education	6.5	4.2	2	6.5	2.5
% college age enrolled	40	10	–	–	–
college enrollment per 1,000	30	6.5	–	9.5	–
graduates % of labor force	7.6	3.1	–	4.7	–
economic, business, and commercial universities	200	30	130	–	–

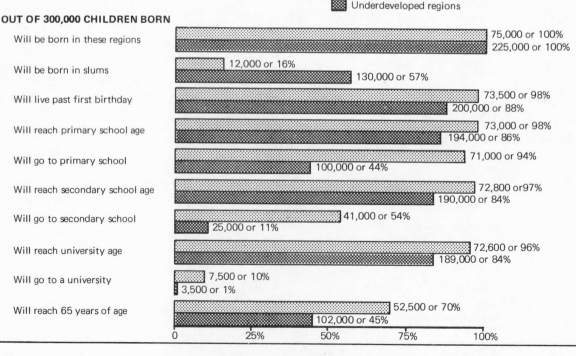

WORLD EDUCATION

Developed regions
Underdeveloped regions

OUT OF 300,000 CHILDREN BORN

Will be born in these regions — 75,000 or 100% / 225,000 or 100%
Will be born in slums — 12,000 or 16% / 130,000 or 57%
Will live past first birthday — 73,500 or 98% / 200,000 or 88%
Will reach primary school age — 73,000 or 98% / 194,000 or 86%
Will go to primary school — 71,000 or 94% / 100,000 or 44%
Will reach secondary school age — 72,800 or 97% / 190,000 or 84%
Will go to secondary school — 41,000 or 54% / 25,000 or 11%
Will reach university age — 72,600 or 96% / 189,000 or 84%
Will go to a university — 7,500 or 10% / 3,500 or 1%
Will reach 65 years of age — 52,500 or 70% / 102,000 or 45%

0   25%   50%   75%   100%

great range of specialized personnel required to or-
ganize our forward world development. People and
their developed intellectual and social competence
are our prime 'natural' resource.

The number of illiterates in the world has risen
by almost 60 million to about 800 million. . . . In
many parts of the world the net effect is only a
slowing down of the increase in the number of

illiterates. In 1960, the organization estimated, there
were 740 million such adult illiterates, or 39.3 percent of the total adult population of 1,881,000,00.
By 1970 . . . there will be 800 million illiterates in
total adult population of 2,225,000,000.[89]

Rene Maheau, Director General of UNESCO,
stated in 1964 that two-fifths of the adult population of the globe cannot read or write—more than
700 million people. This situation has not improved.
In certain areas of the developing countries the illiteracy runs as high as 90 percent of the total population and in many countries the female population is
almost entirely illiterate.

No schooling is available for only about 45 percent of the world's 550 million children between the
ages of 5 and 14.

Full access to the world communication systems—
radio, TV, newspapers, etc.—which are part of the
education process, is also not presently available to
millions around the world. According to estimates
the number of illiterates is rising by 20 to 25 million
persons each year.

UNESCO has suggested that efficacious mass communications can be assured when for every 100
inhabitants of any country, there are at least 10
copies of a daily newspaper, 5 radio sets, 2 cinema
seats, and 2 television receivers. This minimum has
not been attained by 2,000 million people; one hundred states in Asia, Africa and Latin America fall
below this level. [90]

On the average, television in our lives is watched
5½ hours per day. Before entering school children
will have spent 3,000–4,000 hours in front of a television set. By the time they finish high school they
will probably have seen some 15,000 hours of tele-

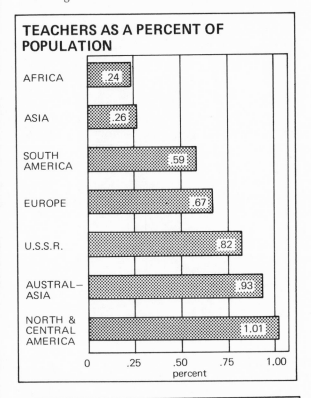

TEACHERS AS A PERCENT OF POPULATION

- AFRICA .24
- ASIA .26
- SOUTH AMERICA .59
- EUROPE .67
- U.S.S.R. .82
- AUSTRAL-ASIA .93
- NORTH & CENTRAL AMERICA 1.01

0   .25   .50   .75   1.00
percent

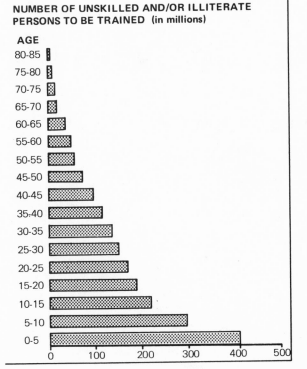

NUMBER OF UNSKILLED AND/OR ILLITERATE PERSONS TO BE TRAINED (in millions)

AGE

80-85
75-80
70-75
65-70
60-65
55-60
50-55
45-50
40-45
35-40
30-35
25-30
20-25
15-20
10-15
5-10
0-5

0   100   200   300   400   500

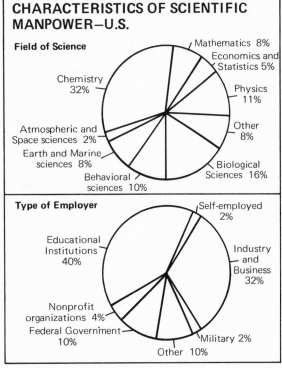

CHARACTERISTICS OF SCIENTIFIC MANPOWER—U.S.

Field of Science

- Mathematics 8%
- Economics and Statistics 5%
- Physics 11%
- Other 8%
- Biological Sciences 16%
- Behavioral sciences 10%
- Earth and Marine sciences 8%
- Atmospheric and Space sciences 2%
- Chemistry 32%

Type of Employer

- Self-employed 2%
- Industry and Business 32%
- Military 2%
- Other 10%
- Federal Government 10%
- Nonprofit organizations 4%
- Educational Institutions 40%

WORLD DISTRIBUTION OF RESEARCH INPUTS AND OUTPUTS

	A	A + B	A + B + C	D
NUMBER OF COUNTRIES	2	7	18	109
PERCENT OF WORLD POPULATION (MID 1970)	12	20	25	72
PERCENT OF WORLD PRODUCTION OF CRUDE STEEL (1962)	52	85	88	11
PERCENT OF WORLD CONSUMPTION OF ENERGY (1964)	46	62	71	25
PERCENT OF WORLD GNP (1969)	51	71	83	16
PERCENT OF GNP SPENT ON EDUCATION (1969)	4.2	4.2	4.1	4.1
PERCENT OF WORLD PROTON ACCELERATORS 1 BEV (1963)	66	92	100	0
PERCENT OF WORLD COMPUTERS (1970)	62	85	93	7
PERCENT OF OUTPUTS OF NUCLEAR POWER PLANTS (MID 1970)	59	83	94	6
PERCENT OF OUTPUT OF PAPERS IN CHEMICAL ABSTRACTS (1960)	46	76	–	–

A	U.S., U.S.S.R.
A + B	U.S., U.S.S.R., UNITED KINGDOM, JAPAN, WEST GERMANY, FRANCE, AUSTRALIA
A + B + C	U.S., U.S.S.R., UNITED KINGDOM, JAPAN, WEST GERMANY, FRANCE, AUSTRALIA, ITALY, SWITZERLAND, DENMARK, ISRAEL, BELGIUM, RUMANIA, POLAND, CANADA, SWEDEN, CZECHOSLOVAKIA
D	127 LESSER DEVELOPED COUNTRIES

vision compared with 10,000 hours spent in formal schooling.

The world spends $100 a year to teach a child how to read and a little later on in life, $7,800 a year to teach him how to shoot. . . . Comparative statistics on education and military budgets make the point: the world as a whole spends $110 billion on public education, and $159 billion—40 percent more—on armaments every year.[91]

. . . The present flow of skilled and qualified personnel from poor to rich countries actually outnumbers the number of advisory personnel going from rich to poor. In 1967 the developing countries obtained the services of 16,000 foreign advisers . . . but the U.N. estimates that close to 40,000 of their own national professionals emigrated to the developed countries. . . . (on research) The wealthy countries have rarely attempted to focus the energies of their enormous scientific and research establishments to help solve specific problems affecting developing countries.[92]

Malnutrition is common.

The FAO estimates that at least a third to a half of the world's people suffer from hunger or nutritional deprivation. The average person in a high-standard area consumes four pounds of food a day as compared with an average pound and a quarter in a low-standard area.

Infant mortality is high.

Infant deaths per 1,000 live births are four times as high in the developing countries as in the developed countries (110 compared with 27).

Life expectancy is low.

A man in the West can expect to live 40 percent longer than the average man in the developing countries and twice as long as the average man in some of the African countries.

Illiteracy is widespread.

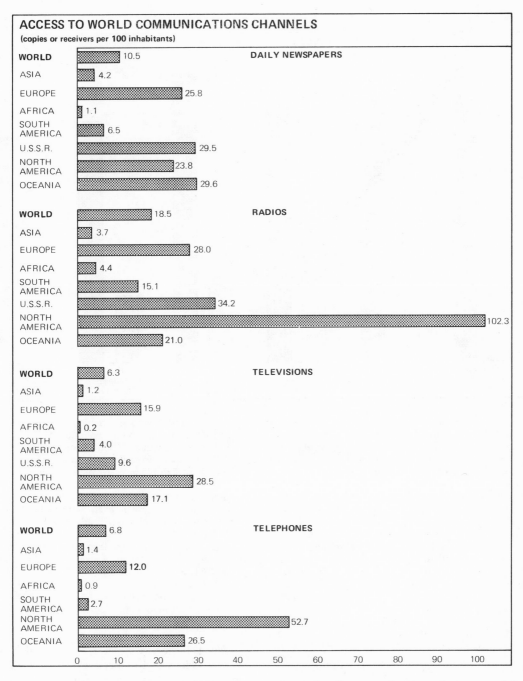

ACCESS TO WORLD COMMUNICATIONS CHANNELS
(copies or receivers per 100 inhabitants)

DAILY NEWSPAPERS

WORLD	10.5
ASIA	4.2
EUROPE	25.8
AFRICA	1.1
SOUTH AMERICA	6.5
U.S.S.R.	29.5
NORTH AMERICA	23.8
OCEANIA	29.6

RADIOS

WORLD	18.5
ASIA	3.7
EUROPE	28.0
AFRICA	4.4
SOUTH AMERICA	15.1
U.S.S.R.	34.2
NORTH AMERICA	102.3
OCEANIA	21.0

TELEVISIONS

WORLD	6.3
ASIA	1.2
EUROPE	15.9
AFRICA	0.2
SOUTH AMERICA	4.0
U.S.S.R.	9.6
NORTH AMERICA	28.5
OCEANIA	17.1

TELEPHONES

WORLD	6.8
ASIA	1.4
EUROPE	12.0
AFRICA	0.9
SOUTH AMERICA	2.7
NORTH AMERICA	52.7
OCEANIA	26.5

There are 100 million more illiterates today than there were 20 years ago, bringing the total number to some 800 million.

Unemployment is endemic and growing.

The equivalent of approximately 20 percent of the entire male labor force is unemployed, and in many areas the urban population is growing twice as fast as the number of urban jobs.[93].

Every half minute, 100 children are born in developing countries. Twenty of them will die within the year. Of the 80 who survive, 60 will have no access to modern medical care during their childhood. An equal number will suffer from malnutrition during their crucial early years, with the possibility of irreversible physical and mental damage. Their chances of dying early will be 20 to 40 times higher than if they lived in Europe or in North America.

Of those who live to school age, only a little more than half will ever set foot in a classroom, and less than 4 out of 10 of those who do will complete the elementary grades.

Consider the sheer magnitude of the problem. Approximately three-quarters of the world's children live in areas where the average income is less than $500 a year. In the less-developed regions of the world, the number of children under 15 increased by about 257 million during the last 11 years to the present total of some 1,052,000,000. In most developing countries they comprise more than 40 percent of the population; in some over half. And through the decade of the 1970s, their numbers are expected to increase another 270 million. In the more developed countries, the child population of the same age has grown only some 13 million in the past decade and is expected to increase another 20 million during the seventies.[94]

The distribution of income and wealth is severely

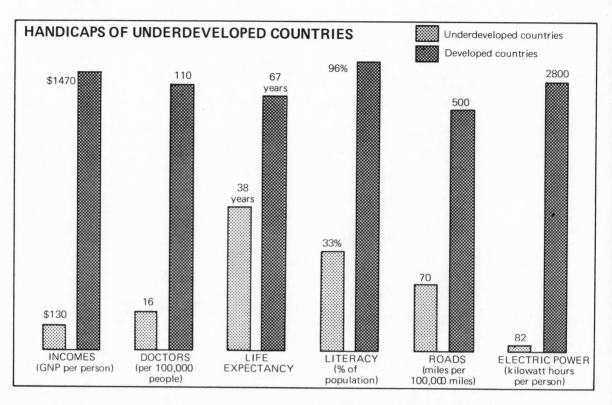

HANDICAPS OF UNDERDEVELOPED COUNTRIES

Underdeveloped countries
Developed countries

INCOMES (GNP per person)	DOCTORS (per 100,000 people)	LIFE EXPECTANCY	LITERACY (% of population)	ROADS (miles per 100,000 miles)	ELECTRIC POWER (kilowatt hours per person)
$130 / $1470	16 / 110	38 years / 67 years	33% / 96%	70 / 500	82 / 2800

skewed, and in some countries becoming more so. In India, 12 percent of the rural families control more than half of the cultivated land. In Brazil, less than 10 percent of the families control 75 percent of the land. In Pakistan, the disparity in per capita income between East and West, which amounted to 18 percent in 1950, became 25 percent in 1960, 31 percent in 1965 and 38 percent in 1970.

The gap between the per capita incomes of the rich nations and the poor nations is widening rather than narrowing, both relatively and absolutely.

The U.S. population is expected to more than double, growing from 152 million in 1950 to 320 million in 2000. But because this population is expected to greatly increase its consumption of energy, its impact on the environment will more than double. Each of those 320 million Americans will represent an electric power consumption of twelve and a half 1950 Americans. Or to put it another way, the effect on the environment from power production of our population in 2000 will be equal to the effect of 4 billion 1950 Americans.[95]

But on the world scene, even the 1950 American was far from typical in energy consumed. For example, in India, per capita consumption of electric power in 1965 was 68.6 kilowatt hours. It was 95 times that in the United States (1968). We think of the population of India as very much larger than that of the U.S., and so it is—over twice as large. But in terms of electric energy use and its related environmental intrusions, one American represents 95 Indians: the effect on environment of our population today with respect to electric energy use is equal to that of 19.2 billion Indians! By 2000 it will be equal to that of well over 116 billion 1965 Indians.

The U.S. currently imports roughly $10 billion of commodities and manufactures from the poor nations. The European Common Market imports more, about $12 billion.

Today, approximately 80 percent of the total financial flows from rich nations to poor nations is accounted for by trade, not aid. Aid and private investment together amount to only 20 percent.

Total exports from the poor nations as a group will run about $50 bllion in 1970, having grown roughly six percent each year over the past ten years. But despite this encouraging growth, the exports of rich countries have grown even faster: thus, the poor countries' share of world trade has been declining. It has, in fact, been declining for the last twenty years: in 1950, exports from the poor nations accounted for 30 percent of world trade; in 1960, 20 percent; and today they represent less than 18 percent of world trade.

The poor nations as a group are, therefore, becoming ever more dependent upon the economic and trade policies of the rich nations.[96]

We should underline here, finally, that in terms of future options and alternatives, that the solution(s) to our most critical world problems are indeed well within our developing scientific and technological capabilities—but it will require a more massive undertaking than is presently evident in our pious hopes and reliance on traditional practices.

For example, our global defense establishments currently encompass a very large fraction of the highest scientific and technical expertise available in the world.

The cost of one modern heavy bomber is this: A brick school in more than 30 cities. It is two electric power plants, each serving a town of 60,000 population. It is two fine, fully equipped hospitals.

We pay for a single fighter plane with a half million bushels of wheat.

We pay for a single destroyer with new homes that could have housed 8,000 people. . . .[97]

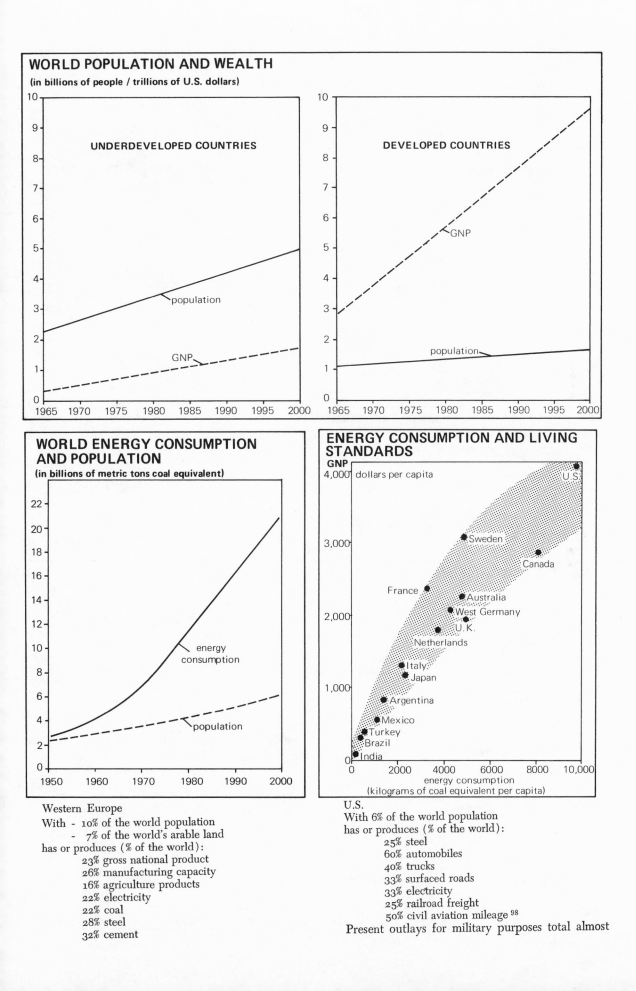

WORLD POPULATION AND WEALTH

(in billions of people / trillions of U.S. dollars)

UNDERDEVELOPED COUNTRIES

population

GNP

DEVELOPED COUNTRIES

GNP

population

WORLD ENERGY CONSUMPTION AND POPULATION

(in billions of metric tons coal equivalent)

energy consumption

population

ENERGY CONSUMPTION AND LIVING STANDARDS

GNP
4,000 dollars per capita

3,000

U.S.

Sweden

Canada

France
Australia
West Germany
2,000
U.K.
Netherlands

Italy
Japan

1,000

Argentina

Mexico
Turkey
Brazil
0 India

energy consumption
(kilograms of coal equivalent per capita)

Western Europe
With - 10% of the world population
- 7% of the world's arable land
has or produces (% of the world):
23% gross national product
26% manufacturing capacity
16% agriculture products
22% electricity
22% coal
28% steel
32% cement

U.S.
With 6% of the world population
has or produces (% of the world):
25% steel
60% automobiles
40% trucks
33% surfaced roads
33% electricity
25% railroad freight
50% civil aviation mileage [98]
Present outlays for military purposes total almost

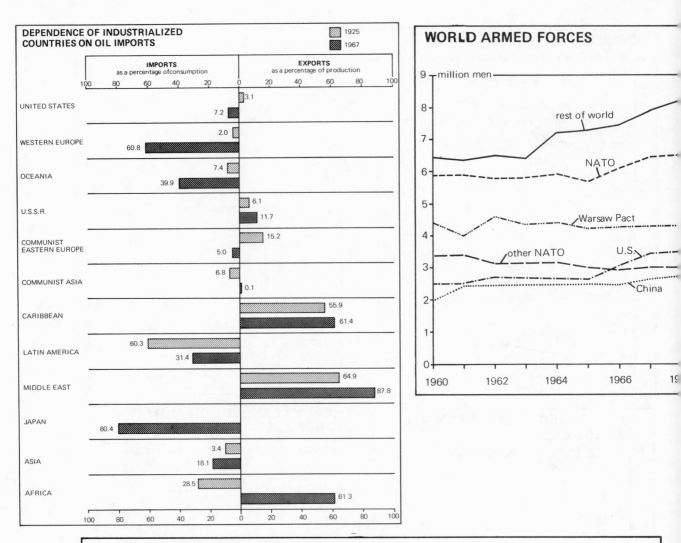

TRENDS IN WORLD MILITARY EXPENDITURES

| | Average per cent change per year | | | | | | Size of military expenditure in 1968 US $ bn, current prices and exchange-rates |
| | Long-term trend 1949–68 | Short-term trend 1965–68 | Year-to-year changes | | | Budgeted change in 1969 | |
			1965–66	1966–67	1967–68		
United States	+ 7.7	+12.0	+19.2	+15.4	+ 2.0	− 0.6	79.5
Other NATO	+ 5.3	+ 1.6	+ 0.9	+ 4.7	− 0.9	+ 0.4	24.4
Total NATO	**+ 7.1**	**+ 9.3**	**+14.1**	**+12.8**	**+ 1.3**	**− 0.4**	104.0
USSR	+ 4.0	+ 9.3	+ 4.7	+ 8.0	+15.5	+ 5.9	18.6 or 39.8^c
Other Warsaw Pact	+ 7.1	+10.9	+ 7.2	+ 7.4	+18.5	+12.8	13.4 or 6.3^c
Total Warsaw Pact	**+ 4.1**	**+ 9.5**	**+ 5.0**	**+ 7.9**	**+15.9**	**+ 6.8**	32.0 or 46.1^c
Other European	+ 5.2	+ 2.0	+ 3.1	− 0.3	+ 3.2	+ 0.3	2.5
Middle East	+12.8	+19.9	+ 8.2	+32.5	+20.0	..	2.7
South Asia	+ 5.2	− 2.5	+ 1.9	−11.7	+ 3.0	..	1.9
Far East (excl. China)	+ 6.5	+ 8.4	+ 0.7	+10.3	+14.8	..	4.0
Oceania	+ 7.9	+17.7	+18.9	+18.2	+16.1	..	1.4
Africa	..	+ 7.6	+11.5	[+ 1.4]	[+10.0]	..	1.2
Central America	+ 3.2	+ 5.2	+ 9.7	+ 5.1	[+ 1.1]	..	0.5
South America	+ 2.7	+ 3.7	− 9.3	+12.8	[+ 8.8]	..	2.1
World	**+ 5.9**	**+ 8.9**	**+10.2**	**+10.7**	**+ 5.8**	..	159.3 or 173.4^c

COMPARATIVE INDICATORS 89

ALTERNATIVE SOCIAL COSTS

NEGATIVE	vs.	POSITIVE
4 attack submarines at $45,000,000 each	would pay for	1 year of agricultural aid for $178,699,760
One $105,000,000 atomic submarine minus missiles	would pay for	$132,095,000 in famine relief aid including freight costs
One $122,600,000 atomic submarine including missiles	would pay for	$150,000,000 in technical aid
One $275,000,000 aircraft carrier	would pay for	$251,000,000 for 12,000 high school dwellings
One $104,616,800 naval weapons plant	would pay for	35 school buildings at $4,000,000 each
One $104,616,800 naval weapons plant	would pay for	26 160-bed hospitals at $4,000,000 each
One $250,000,000 intercontinental ballistic missile base	would pay for	One 1,743,000 KWH capacity hydro-electric dam
14 standard jet bombers at a cost of $8,000,000 each	would pay for	A school lunch program of $110,000,000 and serving 14 million children
One new prototype bomber fully equipped	would pay for	250,000 teacher salaries this year or 30 science faculties each with 1,000 students or 75 fully-equipped 100-bed hospitals . . . or 50,000 tractors . . . or 15,000 harvesters

MILITARY PERSONNEL—AVERAGE COST PER MAN

	COST
U.S.A.	$4,345
Belgium	1,814
Greece	430
Thailand	400
China (Taiwan)	218
Korea	145

ten percent of the world's annual output of goods and services—and over 50 million people are presently occupied with the maintenance of the networks of armed forces, bases, communication services, research, development and production facilities.

One of the greatest priorities which now faces us is how we may turn such negative forces to positive advantage—to apply our cooperative energies to those human problems which threaten the very survival of our societies.

CHART REFERENCES

PAGE

1 INCREASE IN TRAVEL SPEED
"Deadline for Survival," Peter Goldmark, Transactions of the New York Academy of Sciences, Vol. 31, No. 5, 1969, p. 587.

2 THE SPEED OF CHANGE
Adapted from: "Science, Technology, and Change," John McHale, The Annals of the American Academy of Political and Social Science, Vol. 373, September, 1967, p. 120.

3 SHRINKING OF OUR PLANET BY MAN'S INCREASED TRAVEL AND COMMUNICATION SPEEDS AROUND THE GLOBE
The Ecological Context, John McHale, 1970, p. 71.

4 WORLD POPULATION
"Deadline for Survival," p. 585.

4 LIFE EXPECTANCY
"Deadline for Survival," p. 585.

5 THE INCREASE OF POPULATION
The Dynamics of Change, Don Fabun, Kaiser Aluminum Corporation, Prentice-Hall, Inc., 1967., p. 12.

5 INCREASE IN EXPLOSIVE POWER AND KILLING AREA
Technology and Social Change, Allen et al, Appleton-Century-Crofts, Inc., New York, 1957, p. 37.

7 COMPOSITION OF THE BIOSPHERE
"Mineral Cycles," Edward S. Deevey, Jr., Scientific American, September, 1970, p. 150.

8 THE EARTH'S BIOSPHERE
"The Biosphere," G. Evelyn Hutchinson, Scientific American, September, 1970, p. 45.
"Technological Forecasting Techniques in Britain." T. Garrett, Technological Forecasting and Corporate Strategy, Wils et al, American Elsevier Publishing Company, Inc., New York, 1969, p. 237, and other sources.

10 GLOBAL BIOMASS—HUMAN SPHERE
The Hungry Planet, Georg Borgstrom, Macmillan Co., 1967.

14 WORLD CARBON DIOXIDE BALANCE
Adapted from: "Carbon Dioxide and Climate," Gilbert N. Plass, Scientific American, July, 1959, p. 6.
"Increase of Exchange Carbon in the Earth's Reservoirs from Combustion of Fossil Fuels," Doris J. Dugas, RAND Corporation (A.D. 680-747), December, 1968, p. 5.

15 NATURAL AND MAN-MADE TRACE-GAS CYCLES
"The Global Circulation of Atmospheric Pollutants," Reginald E. Newell, Scientific American, January, 1971, p. 37.

15 TRENDS AFFECTING AIR POLLUTION—U.S.
"The Air We Breathe," Dr. J. Middleton, Population Bulletin, Vol. 24, No. 5, December, 1968, p. 117.

15 SULPHUR DIOXIDE CONCENTRATIONS
Civilization at the Crossroads, Radovan Richta, International Arts and Sciences Press, Prague, 1969, p. 345.

16 TONS OF POLLUTANTS EMITTED ANNUALLY —U.S.
The Sources of Air Pollution, U.S. Department of Health, Education, and Welfare, Public Health Service Publication No. 1548, September, 1968.

16 AIR POLLUTION AND HUMAN ECOLOGICAL EFFECTS
"A Model of Society," Environmental System Group, Institute of Ecology, University of California at Davis, April, 1969.

17 SOURCES OF AIR POLLUTION—U.S.
"The Air We Breathe," p. 115.

17 AUTOMOTIVE POLLUTION
Adapted from: Social Development, U.S. Department of Health, Education and Welfare, 1966, p. 24. Waste Management and Control, National Academy of Sciences, 1966, p. 242.

17 WORLD PRODUCTION OF FOSSIL FUELS AND CARBON DIOXIDE PRODUCED
Restoring the Quality of our Environment, Report of the Environmental Pollution Panel, President's Science Advisory Committee, The White House, November, 1965, pp. 116-117.

18 CARBON MONOXIDE EMISSIONS—U.S.
Global Effects of Environmental Pollution, Edited by S. Fred Singer, Springer–Verlag, New York, 1970, p. 35.

18 GLOBAL EMISSIONS OF CARBON MONOXIDE
Global Effects of Environmental Pollution, p. 60.

19 PROPORTION OF LAND USE: WORLD AND REGIONAL
"Why the Global Income Gap Grows Wider," Charlton Ogburn, Jr., Population Bulletin, Vol. 26, No. 2, Population Reference Bureau, June 2, 1970, p. 12.

20 PER CAPITA USE OF SELECTED FUELS, COPPER AND AGRICULTURAL MINERALS
World Resources Production 50 Years of Change, H. V. Warren and E. F. Wilks, B.C. Geographical Series, 1966, (Quoted in "An Environmental Atlas," Dr. C. S. Holling, Director, Institute of Human Ecology, University of British Columbia, Vancouver, Canada).

20 FERTILIZER CONSUMPTION AND AGRICULTURAL LAND
"Human Food Production as a Process in the Biosphere," Lester R. Brown, Scientific American, September, 1970, p. 165.

21 INCREASE IN FERTILIZER CONSUMPTION
"Human Food Production as a Process in the Biosphere," p. 164.

21 ENVIRONMENTAL EFFECTS
Environmental Effects of Weapons Technology, McClintock et al, Scientists Institute for Public Information, New York, 1970, p. 20.

21 BIOLOGICAL MAGNIFICATION OF DDT
Time, July 11, 1969, p. 56.

23 TOTAL REFUSE PRODUCTION—U.S.
Waste Management and Control, National Academy of Sciences, Washington, D.C., Publication 1400, p. 133.

23 REFUSE PRODUCTION PER PERSON—U.S.
Why Fusion?, William C. Gough, U.S. Atomic Energy Commission, June, 1970, p. 275.

23 URBAN INPUTS AND OUTPUTS—U.S.
Adapted from: Diagrams, Arthur Lockwood, Watson-Guptill, New York, 1969.

24 AVERAGE COMPOSITION OF MUNICIPAL
REFUSE
"Closing the Cycle from Use to Reuse," The Fusion
Torch, May, 1969, U.S. Atomic Energy Commission, Washington, D.C., p. 6.

24 GROWTH IN ACCUMULATED SOLID WASTE
"Closing the Cycle from Use to Reuse," p. 6.

24 COST OF REFUSE CONTROL–U.S.
Waste Management and Control, p. 250.

24 GROWTH IN LAND AREA REQUIRED FOR
DISPOSAL OF SOLID WASTE–U.S.
"Closing the Cycle from Use to Reuse," p. 6.

25 THE HYDROSPHERE
The Ecological Context, p. 46.

26 WORLD MARINE FOOD CATCH
FAO Yearbook of Fishery Statistics, Vol. 27, 1968.
The Ecological Context, p. 102.

26 SOURCE AND USE OF WORLD MARINE FOOD
CATCH
FAO Yearbook of Fishery Statistics, Vol. 27, 1968.
The Ecological Context, p. 102.

27 CONSUMPTION OF WORLD MARINE FOOD
CATCH
FAO Yearbook of Fishery Statistics, Vol. 27, 1968.
The Ecological Context, p. 102.

28 WATER USE IN THE U.S.–1900-1980
Statistical Abstracts of the U.S., U.S. Department of
Commerce, Bureau of the Census, 86th edition,
1965, p. 173.

28 ANNUAL WORLD WATER REQUIREMENTS
BY YEAR 2000
The World's Water Resources, Present and Future,
G. P. Kalinin and V. D. Bykov; Impacts of Science
on Society, Vol. XIX, No. 2, April–June, 1969.

29 WATER CONSUMPTION PATTERN–U.S.
Water and Waste Water Engineering I, Gordon Fair,
et al, John Wiley and Sons, New York, 1966, p. 13.

29 WATER REQUIRED FOR FOOD PRODUCTION
Too Many, Georg Borgstrom, Macmillan, New York,
p. 153.

33 DAILY HUMAN METABOLIC TURNOVER
Document Six, John McHale, 1967, p. 43.

33 HISTORICAL LIFE EXPECTANCIES
Health and Disease, Rene Dubos, Maya Pines, and
editors of Life, Time, Inc., New York, 1965, pp.
193–195.

34 THE GROWTH OF HUMAN NUMBERS
"How Many People Have Ever Lived on Earth?",
Annabelle Desmond, Population Bulletin, Population
Reference Bureau, Vol. 18, No. 1, February, 1962,
p. 5.

35 WORLD POPULATION GROWTH
The Ten Year Program, John McHale, 1966, p. 8.

36 MAJOR AREAS OF WORLD POPULATION
The Ecological Context, p. 93.

37 WORLD POPULATION
Adapted from: "1970 World Population Data
Sheet," Population Reference Bureau, April, 1970.

38 WORLD POPULATION GROWTH IN DE-
VELOPED AND UNDERDEVELOPED
REGIONS–1910-2050
"The Role of Goals and Planning in the Solution of
the World Food Problem," Hasan Ozbekhan, Mankind 2000, edited by Robert Jungk and Johan
Galtung, 1969, p. 120.

39 WORLDWIDE FOOD ENERGY
"Human Food Production as a Process in the Biosphere," p. 166.

39 PRODUCTION OF BASIC FOODSTUFFS
"Food Storage in the Developing Countries," Dr.
D. W. Hall, The Journal of the Royal Society for
the Encouragement of Arts, Manufacturers, and
Commerce, London, England, July, 1969, p. 563.

40 WHEAT YIELDS IN MEXICO, PAKISTAN,
AND INDIA
Seeds of Change, Lester R. Brown, 1970, p. 37.

41 WORLD CONSUMPTION OF PROTEIN
"The Food Resources of the Oceans," S. Holt,
Scientific American, September, 1969, p. 188.

41 WORLD CONSUMPTION OF CALORIES
Human Trends and Needs, R. B. Fuller and John
McHale, World Resources Inventory, Southern
Illinois University, Carbondale, 1963, p. 40.

42 MEDICAL ADVANCES, LIFE EXPECTANCIES,
AND POPULATION
The Future of the Future, John McHale, 1969, p.
165.

44 NUMBER OF YEARS SPENT IN LIFE
ACTIVITIES
Human Trends and Needs, p. 16.

45 LABOR FORCE SHIFT IN TYPICAL ADVANCED
ECONOMY
Civilization at the Crossroads, p. 325.

45 DEGREE OF INDUSTRIALIZATION
Science Policy News, November, 1969, p. 52.

45 MAN, ANIMAL, AND MECHANICAL ENERGY
USED IN PRODUCTION–U.S.
The Future of the Future, p. 279.

46 HISTORICAL ANNUAL AVERAGE WORK-
WEEK–U.S.
The Year 2000, Herman Kahn and Anthony Wiener,
Hudson Institute, 1967.

47 RELATIONSHIP OF MAN TO THE
ELECTROMAGNETIC SPECTRUM
Human Trends and Needs, p. 12.

47 TOTAL BOOKS PUBLISHED
"Deadline for Survival" p. 588.

47 SOURCES OF THE WORLD'S CHEMICAL
LITERATURE–1966
American Chemical Society, 1968.

48 INCREASE OF KNOWLEDGE–THE
ELECTROMAGNETIC SPECTRUM
The Ecological Context, p. 68; "Time: Its Breadth
and Depth in Biological Rhythms," J. J. Grebe,
Annals of the New York Academy of Sciences, Vol.
98, October 30, 1962.

48 ELECTROMAGNETIC SPECTRUM
The Ecological Context, p. 76.

50 WORLD TOURISM
U.N. International Tourist Year, 1967, Office of
Public Information.

50 WORLD AIR CARGO PROJECTIONS
Barclay's Bank Review, November, 1969.

50 NUMBER OF INTERNATIONAL CON-
FERENCES HELD
The Future of the Future, p. 272.

53 STAGES OF TECHNOLOGY
The Ecological Context, p. 82.

54 MAN'S VERTICAL MOBILITY
Compiled from various sources.

55 SPEED TREND CURVE
"The Measurement of Knowledge and Technology,"
Daniel Bell, Indicators of Social Change, edited by
Sheldon and Moore, 1968, p. 188.

56 WORLD COMPUTER POPULATION
"Computers in Eastern Europe," Ivan Berenyi,
Scientific American, October, 1970, p. 104.

57 COMPUTER PERFORMANCE
The Ecological Context, p. 58; "Computer Aspects
of Technological Change, Automation and Economic
Progress," P. Armer, RAND Corporation, November,
1965.

57 TREND TOWARD MINIATURIZATION
"Automation Surge," Science News Letter, (84:294),
November 9, 1963; "The Exchange," Frank Leary,
New York Stock Exchange, January, 1965. "Minia-
turisation ad Infinitum," G. W. Dummer, New
Scientist, February 25, 1965.

58 COMPUTER STORAGE COSTS
"Systems for Remote-Sensing Information and Distribution," Vol. 8, Useful Applications of Earth-
Oriented Satellites, NAS-NAC, Washington, 1969,
p. 42.

58 DIGITAL CAPACITY AND COMPUTING SPEED
The Emerging Composites, A. L. Adams and L. L.
Dachs, p. 67.

58 PACKING DENSITIES OF MICROELECTRONIC
SYSTEMS
"Bioengineering Research," Glenn Edmonson, Bioengineering, edited by George Bugliarello, San Francisco Press, Inc., 1968, p. 376.

59 INSTRUMENTATION POTENTIALLY RE-
QUIRED OF EARTH RESOURCES SURVEYS
Aerospace Technology, November 20, 1967.

60 THE EARTH'S ENERGY FLUX
"Energy Resources," M. K. Hubbert, National Academy of Sciences, 1962.

61 ENERGY SYSTEMS
"The Nature and Sources of Energy," Zimmerman,
Introduction to World Resources, Frederick A.
Praeger, Inc., New York, 1966, p. 68. "Energy R. &
D. and National Progress," Inter-Department Energy
Study, Washington, D.C., 1964, p. 40.

62 THE RISE OF WORLD ENERGY SOURCES
Energy into Power, Sterland, National History Press,
Garden City, 1967, pp. 120-121.

63 REMAINING FOSSIL FUEL SUPPLIES—
WORLD
"Human Energy Production as a Process in the
Biosphere," S. Fred Singer, Scientific American,
September, 1970, p. 184.

63 LIFETIMES OF FOSSIL FUEL SUPPLIES
"Mined Out! Our Diminishing Mineral Resources,"
Preston Cloud, The Ecologist, Vol. 1 and 1, August,
1970, p. 27.

63 POTENTIAL MARINE ENERGY SOURCES

The Ecological Context, p. 124. "Earth Sciences and
Oceanography," Robert Colbarn, editor, Modern
Science and Technology, 1965, p. 622.

64 PROJECTION OF MAJOR NUCLEAR POWER
PROGRAMS TO 1976
Science Policy News, Vol. 2, No. 2, September,
1970, p. 24.

64 NUCLEAR PROGRAMS IN SELECTED
COUNTRIES
Civilization at the Crossroads, p. 294.

65 WORLD URANIUM DEMAND
Uranium Production and Short Term Demand, Report by the European Nuclear Energy Agency and
the International Atomic Energy Agency—OECD,
January, 1969.

65 EXPECTED GROWTH OF WORLD ENERGY
CONSUMPTION
Barclay's Bank Review, May, 1969.

66 WORLD ENERGY FLOW—1964
The Ecological Context, p. 70; Major sources: Pro-
ceedings of the International Conference on Peace-
ful Uses of Atomic Energy, Vol. 1, "The World's
Requirements for Energy: The Role of Nuclear
Energy," United Nations, New York, 1956. "World
Energy Supplies 1961-1964," United Nations, New
York, 1966.

66 WORLD ENERGY PRODUCTION—1965
From various sources.

66 WORLD ENERGY CONSUMPTION—1966
From various sources.

67 WORLD CONSUMPTION OF ENERGY
SOURCES
Barclay's Bank Review, May, 1969.

67 HUMAN AFFAIRS IN TIME PERSPECTIVE
Energy Resources, M. King Hubert, U.S. National
Academy of Sciences, 1962.

68 TOTAL ENERGY CONSUMPTION—U.S.
"Human Energy Production as a Process in the Biosphere," S. Fred Singer, p. 184.

68 TRENDS IN ELECTRIC UTILITY FUEL
CONSUMPTION
"Fuels," James O'Connor, Power special report,
June, 1968, p. 4.

70 ENERGY CONVERSION EFFICIENCIES
The Ecological Context, p. 51.

70 OVERALL EFFICIENCIES OF STEAM
ELECTRIC PLANTS
Environmental Cost of Electric Power, Dean Abra-
hamson, Scientists' Institute for Public Information,
New York, 1970, p. 7.

70 EFFICIENCY OF ENERGY CONVERSION
SYSTEMS
"The Measurement of Knowledge and Technology,"
p. 190.

71 RELATIVE ABUNDANCE OF ELEMENTS IN
THE SEA
"Metals and Mineral Processing—How Minerals are
Recovered," Marshall F. Sittig, Engineering and
Mineral Journal, June, 1958.

71 RELATIVE ABUNDANCE OF ELEMENTS IN
THE EARTH
"The Physical Resources of the Ocean," E. Wenk,
Jr., Scientific American, September, 1969, p. 171.

72 WORLD PRODUCTION OF MAJOR MINERALS AND METALS BY COUNTRY
The Ecological Context, pp. 162-163.

73 WORLD STEEL CONSUMPTION
"Human Materials as a Process in the Biosphere," Harrison Brown, Scientific American, September, 1970, p. 198.

74 INDUSTRIAL REGENERATIVE CYCLE
World Trends Exhibit, John McHale, p. 11.

75 POPULATION/MATERIALS: PROJECTED CONSUMPTION
The Future of the Future, p. 233.

74 PROJECTED CONSUMPTION OF MATERIALS
"The Synthetics Age," R. Houwink, Modern Plastics, August, 1966, p. 99.

76 THE EFFECT OF INCREASED POPULATION ON ORE CONSUMPTION
"Closing the Cycle from Use to Reuse," p. 7.

77 MATERIALS REPLACED BY PLASTICS
The Future of the Future, p. 230.

77 LIFETIMES OF WORLD METAL RESERVES
Harrison Brown, p. 205.

78 FOREIGN METALS IN U.S. AUTO
Why Fusion?, p. 269.

78 CONSUMPTION OF PACKAGING MATERIALS
The Role of Packaging in Solid Waste Management 1966 to 1976, A. Darnay and William Franklin, Bureau of Solid Waste Management, U.S. Department of Health, Education and Welfare, 1969, p. 115.

79 DEPLETION OF WORLD RESERVES OF COMMERCIAL GRADE ORES IF WORLD POPULATION HAD U.S. LIVING STANDARD
Why Fusion?, p. 271.

79 WORLD DEMAND FOR PAPER AND BOARD—1975
The Geography of Economic Activity, Conkling and Yeates, McGraw-Hill, New York, 1968, p. 477.

81 URBANIZATION—U.S.
Resources in America's Future, Landsberg, Fischman, and Fisher, Johns Hopkins Press, Baltimore, Maryland, 1963, p. 371.

81 ESTIMATED ANNUAL HOUSING NEEDS
The Ten Year Program, p. 20.

82 THE EDUCATION GAP
Science Policy News, November, 1969, p. 51.

82 WORLD EDUCATION
"Social Planning and Comprehensive Development," Demetrius S. Iatridis, Ekistics, Vol. 18, No. 109, December, 1964. W. Taylor Thom, Jr., World Academy of Art and Science, 1964.

83 CHARACTERISTICS OF SCIENTIFIC MANPOWER—U.S.
National Register of Scientific and Technical Personnel, American Science Manpower, National Science Foundation, 1962, p. 221.

83 TEACHERS AS A PERCENT OF POPULATION
"Educational Training and Technology," Robert C. Williams, Journal of the Royal Society of the Arts, June, 1969, p. 480.

84 WORLD DISTRIBUTION OF RESEARCH INPUTS AND OUTPUTS
Adapted (1971) from original chart of Dr. Stevan Dedijer, University of Lund, Sweden, personal correspondence, February 21, 1966.

85 ACCESS TO WORLD COMMUNICATIONS CHANNELS
"Communications—Key to Man's Self-Awareness," Henry R. Cassirer, Paper presented at the Joint Conference on Environment and Society in Transition of the American Geographical Society and the World Academy of Art and Science, New York, April, 1970.

86 HANDICAPS OF UNDERDEVELOPED COUNTRIES
The U.S. and the World in the 1985 Era, Syracuse Research Corporation, 1964, p. 100.

87 WORLD POPULATION AND WEALTH
"Closing the Cycle from Use to Reuse," p. 8.

87 WORLD ENERGY CONSUMPTION AND POPULATION
The Ecological Context, p. 117.

87 ENERGY CONSUMPTION AND LIVING STANDARDS
Why Fusion?, p. 259.

88 DEPENDENCE OF INDUSTRIALIZED COUNTRIES ON OIL IMPORTS
"International Flows of Energy Sources," Joel Darmstadter, IEEE Spectrum, May, 1970, p. 69.

88 WORLD ARMED FORCES
SIPRI Yearbook of World Armaments and Disarmaments 1968/69, Stockholm International Peace Research Institute, Humanities Press, New York, 1970, p. 71.

88 TRENDS IN WORLD MILITARY EXPENDITURES
SIPRI Yearbook of World Armaments and Disarmaments 1968/69, p. 19.

89 ALTERNATIVE SOCIAL COSTS
The Future of the Future, p. 275, Source: "The Peace Race," Seymour Melman, Braziller, 1961; Atlanta Journal, March 11, 1965.

TEXT REFERENCES

1 "The Environment of Change," Francis Bello, Sterling Forest Conference, New York, June, 1964, p. 9.

2 Rational Use of the Biosphere, World Agriculture 17, October, 1968, pp. 31-35.

3 "The Human Biosphere and its Biological and Chemical Limitations," G. Borgstrom, from Global Impacts of Applied Microbiology, Wiley, New York, 1964, p. 131.

4 Too Many, p. 131.

5 Population Bulletin, Vol. XXVI, No. 2, 1970, Population Reference Bureau, Washington, D.C.

6   The Atmosphere, Thomas F. Malone, Senior Vice President and Director of Research, The Travelers Insurance Company, (From Background Papers for the 13th Annual Conference of the U.S. National Commission for UNESCO).

7   Challenge of Change, W. T. Pecora, Director, U.S. Geological Survey, reprinted from Mining Congress Journal, November, 1970.

8   Report from Center of the Biology of Natural Systems, Vol. 3, Issue 4, September–October, 1970, Washington University, St. Louis, Missouri.

9   OECD Observer, No. 48, October, 1970, p. 13.

10   Air Pollution, Scientists' Institute for Public Information Workbook, 1970, p. 15.

11   Release No. 70-133, NASA, Washington, D.C., Sunday, August 9, 1970.

12   Too Many, p. 131.

13   The Sea: Should We Now Write It Off as the Future Garbage Pit?, R. W. Risebrough, Background Papers for 13th National Conference of the U.S. National Commission for UNESCO, 1969.

14   Air Pollution, Scientists' Institute for Public Information Workbook, 1970, p. 14.

15   The Ecological Context, p. 14.

16   Environmental Health Problems, U.S. Department of Health, Education and Welfare, 1970, p. 4.

17   Environmental Health Problems, p. 4.

18   Use Pollution to Benefit Mankind, J. Leon Potter, Ocean Industry, May, 1969, p. 94.

19   Population Bulletin, Vol. XXVI, No. 2, 1970, Population Reference Bureau, Inc., Washington, D.C.

20   The Sea: Should We Now Write It Off as a Garbage Pit?

21   The Food Resources of the Ocean, S. J. Holt, Scientific American, September, 1969, p. 178.

22   Report from Center for the Biology of Natural Systems, Vol. 3, Issue 4, September–October, 1970, Washington University, St. Louis, Missouri.

23   The Ecology and Politics Manual, Alan S. Miller and Phil Farnham, 491 Guerrero Street, San Francisco, 1970.

24   Extracted from "Oil Pollution of the Ocean," Max Blumer, Woods Hole Oceanographic Institution, Massachusetts.

25   Environmental Health Problems, p. 5.

26   "Use Pollution to Benefit Mankind," J. L. Potter, Ocean Industry, May 1969, pp. 96-97.

27   Population Bulletin, Vol. XXVI, No. 2, 1970, Population Reference Bureau, Inc., Washington, D.C.

28   Human Trends and Needs, R. B. Fuller and J. McHale, World Resources Inventory, Southern Illinois University, Carbondale, 1963, p. 12.

29   Human Trends and Needs, p. 12.

30   "The Environment—and what to do about it," Dr. Glenn T. Seaborg, paper given at meeting of the National Academy of Sciences–National Research Council, Argonne National Laboratory, May 5, 1969, published in Nuclear News, July, 1969).

31   The Ways of Man, J. Gillin, Appleton-Century-Crofts, Educational Division, Meredith Corporation, New York, 1948, p. 290.

32   "Toward a Non-Malthusian Population Policy," Jean Mayer, Columbia Forum, Vol. XII, No. 2, Summer, 1969.

33   Agricultural Productivity in Relation to Population, Colin Clark, in "Man and his Future," edited by Gordon Wolstenholme, published by Little, Brown, and Company, U.S., 1963, p. 30.

34   Hunger, Scientists' Institute for Public Information Workbook, 1970, p. 11.

35   Agriculture/2000, U.S. Department of Agriculture, Washington, D.C., May, 1967, p. 31.

36   Hunger, Roger Revelle, Director, Center for Population Studies, Harvard University, 1970, p. 14.

37   "The Role of Goals and Planning," H. Ozbekhan, in Mankind 2000, edited by R. Jungk and J. Galtung, Allen and Unwin, U.K., 1969.

38   Seeds of Change, p. 4.

39   Seeds of Change, p. 4.

40   Economic and Business Outlook for the Developing Countries in the 1970's: Trends and Issues, James P. Grant, published by the Overseas Development Council, Washington, D.C., 1970.

41   Comments delivered by Assistant Secretary of Agriculture Thomas K. Cowden at 1:30 p.m. on Tuesday, December 9, 1969, before the Natural Resources Conference of the 50th Annual Convention of the American Farm Bureau Federation in Washington, D.C.

42   Agriculture/2000, p. 46.

43   Science and Technology for Development, Vol. I. United Nations, 1963.

44   New York Times, September 23, 1970.

45   U.N. Study on World's Children, February 7, 1970.

46   The Evolution of International Technology, The Science Policy Research and Foreign Affairs Divisions, Legislative Reference Service, Library of Congress, Committee on Foreign Affairs, U.S. House of Representatives, December, 1970.

47   Environmental Health Problems, p. 4.

48   "Experiments in Perception," Adelbert Ames, Jr., Progressive Architecture, December, 1947, p. 20.

49   Promotion of Man, John B. Calhoun, paper for the Symposium on "Global Systems Dynamics," University of Virginia, June 17-19, 1969.

50   Letter to U.N. Secretary-General U Thant, Julian Aleksandrowicz, July 30, 1970.

51   "The Economy, Energy, and the Environment," study prepared by the Environmental Policy Division, Legislative Reference Service, Library of Congress, 91st Congress, 2nd Session, September 1, 1970, p. 1, (U.S. Government Printing Office, Washington, D.C.).

52   "The Post-Industrial Society," Daniel Bell, Liberty Mutual Anniversary Conference, June, 1962.

53   San Francisco Chronicle, Monday, July 7, 1969.

54   The American Challenge, J. J. Servan-Schreiber, 1968.

55   The Evolution of International Technology, The Science Policy Research and Foreign Affairs Division, Legislative Reference Service, Library of Congress, Committee on Foreign Affairs, U.S. House of Representatives, December, 1970.

56   The Population Explosion and the Employment Crisis, James P. Grant, Economic and Business Outlook for the Developing Countries in the 1970's: Trends and Issues, published by the Overseas Development Council, Washington, D.C., 1970.

57   "The Multinational Corporation and the Nation State," Arthur Barber, Institute for Politics and Planning, Washington, D.C., 1968.

58   "The Nation State, The Multi-National Corporation and the Changing World Order," Lester R. Brown, U.S. Department of Agriculture, Washington, D.C., 1968.

59   The Evolution of International Technology, U.S. House of Representatives, December, 1970.

60   "International Regulation of Science and Technology," Allan McKnight, International Journal, Autumn, 1970, pp. 745-746.

61   "Economic Growth: Myth or Reality, William and Helga Woodruff, Technology and Culture, Fall, No. 4, 1966.

62   "Continuity and Change in the International Environment," Lee Stull, Foreign Service Journal, January, 1970, p. 17.

63   Adapted from "Future Computer Technology and Its Impact," W. H. Ware, Office of Technical Services, U.S. Department of Commerce, (D.D. AD 631-941).

64   Chicago Tribune, January 8, 1971, p. 16.

65   "Remote Sensing of Natural Resources," Robert N. Colwell, Scientific American, January, 1968, pp. 54-69.

66   "Results of Space Research 1957-1967," E. R. Spangler, TRW Space Log, Vol. 7, No. 3, Fall, 1967, p. 52.

67   Resources and Man, the Committee on Resources and Man, U.S. National Academy of Sciences–National Research Council, published by W. H. Freeman and Company, San Francisco, 1969.

68   "The Impact of the Nuclear Age," Boris Pregel, America Faces the Nuclear Age, Sheridan House, New York, 1961, pp. 28-29.

69   The Evolution of International Technology, U.S. House of Representatives, December, 1970.

70   Barclay's Bank Review (insert), May, 1969.

71   "Resources and Environment—Quest for Balance, W. T. Pecora, Director, U.S. Geological Survey, reprinted from Mining Congress Journal, August, 1970.

72   Population Bulletin, Population Reference Bureau, Inc., Washington, D.C., June 2, 1970, p. 20-24.

73   "Environmental Side Effects of Energy Pollution," Donald F. Anthrop, Bulletin of the Atomic Scientists, October, 1970, p. 39.

74   Environmental Cost of Electric Power, p. 29-30.

75   Environmental Cost of Electric Power, pp. 29-30.

76   The Geography of World Energy Consumption, R. A. Harper, Department of Geography, Southern Illinois University, 1966.

77   "World Energy Prospects," Sir Harold Hartley, F.R.S., World in 1984, Vol. I, edited by Nigel Calder, Penguin Books, 1965.

78   Population Bulletin, Vol. XXVI, No. 2, June, 1970, Population Reference Bureau, Washington, D.C.

79   World Power Conference 1964, The Times, London, September 9, 1964.

80   Journal of the Royal Society of Arts, December, 1970, p. 38.

81   Annual Report, Global Marine, Inc., 1969.

82   "Where the Food is to Come From, Charleton Ogburn, Jr., Population Bulletin, Population Reference Bureau, Inc., Washington, D.C., June 2, 1970, p. 8.

83   "Resources and Environment—Quest for Balance," W. T. Pecora, Director, U.S. Geological Survey, reprinted from Mining Congress Journal, August, 1970.

84   Population Bulletin, June 2, 1970, pp. 10-12, Population Reference Bureau, Inc., Washington, D.C.

85   Christian Science Monitor, December 2, 1970, p. 15.

86   Environmental Cost of Electric Power, p. 31.

87   Population Bulletin, Vol. XXVI, No. 2, June, 1970, Population Reference Bureau, Inc., Washington, D.C.

88   Study of International Housing, U.S. Senate, 1963.

89   New York Times, October 19, 1969, p. 8.

90   The Evolution of International Technology, U.S. House of Representatives, December, 1970.

91   New York Times, March, 17, 1970.

92   Mayday, No. 21, November, 1969.

93   PRB Selection No. 33, October, 1970, p. 5, Population Reference Bureau, Washington, D.C.

94   U.N. Study on World's Children, February 7, 1970.

95   Environmental Cost of Electric Power, p. 3-4.

96   "World Trade: Engine for Global Progress," Harold Malmgren and Joe Kimmins, Communique on Development Issues, No. 1, Overseas Development Council, Washington, D.C.

97   New York Times, April 17, 1953.

98   National Security Seminar, 1966, p. 156.

INDEX

062817